Hope
Deferred

Finding Peace in the Midst of Infertility

Jillian Heerlyn

Unwavering Hope Press

Notes on Biblical Translation
All scripture quotations, unless otherwise indicated, are taken from the Holy Bible: *New International Version®*, NIV® Copyright © 2011 by Biblica, Inc.® Used by permission. All rights reserved worldwide.

Also used: Scripture quotations marked NIV, 1984 edition are taken from the Holy Bible: *New International Version®*, NIV® Copyright © 1984. Used by permission of Zondervan. All rights reserved worldwide.

Also used: Scripture quotations marked MSG, are taken from The Message®, copyright © 1993, 1994, 1995, 1996, 2000, 2001, 2002 by Eugene Peterson. Used by permission of NavPress Publishing Group. All rights reserved worldwide.

Printed in the United States of America.
First Edition 2020
Library of Congress Control Number:
2020906858
ISBN 978-1-7348888-0-5
eISBN 978-1-7348888-1-2

To my husband, Todd
and my children,
Alliyah, Josh, Noah, and Sofia.

I love you all dearly.

Acknowledgements

To my husband, Todd, who wrangled the kids while I was tucked away getting this book ready to be released. Thank you for bringing me meals so I would not forget to eat. Thank you for distracting our youngest when she stood outside the door asking, "Do you want to build a snowman?" - Thinking I was locked away like Elsa.

To my children, Alliyah, Josh, Noah, and Sofia who gave me time and space to work on this book. Thank you for helping out around the house, for being excited with me, and for understanding why I spent so many days of the coronavirus stay-at-home order "hiding" in my room.

To my mom - Thank you for reading this book and scouring the pages for grammatical errors even though the topic was not your cup of tea.

To all my friends who have prayed for me, encouraged me, and cried with me - both through infertility and in publishing this book. And to all of you who have shamelessly posted on social media to get the word out, thank you.

To Rob Link for introducing me to Jesus and for helping me to grow in knowing Him and becoming like Him. Thank you for reading and reviewing my book and for encouraging me to do great things on this adventure with Jesus.

To Stacie Gryga, David Penning, Liz Jadczak, and Emily Groot for reading my book ahead of time to write a review and offer great feedback. Thank you.

To Dr. William G Dodds and all the staff of The Fertility Center for all your support through the fertility process. Thank you for treating your patients with great care and compassion. Thank you, Dr. Dodds, for contributing to this book and for your enthusiasm and support for me in writing it.

To our New Community Church family , thank you for your prayers and support.

Contents

Preface

I am truly bummed that there is a reason to write a book like this. I want you to know my heart up front. I am genuinely sorry that you find yourself with a reason to read this book. I wish infertility had never occupied a space on your journey.

Since infertility has reared its ugly head in your life, either personally or through a loved one, I imagine you might be a little (or a lot) worn out. I see you as you precariously balance on the edge of your emotions and your questions and hopes and dreams. Your story is unique and special, but one thing we have in common is that this is not an easy road to walk.

I have wrestled long and deep with the Maker of the Universe over the issue of infertility. I have begged Him to create life in me, only to hear silence. Somewhere in the silence, I sensed He was encouraging me to keep talking, to keep pouring out my heart so He could fill it with His truth. I do not know who first coined the phrase, "When you can't see His hand, trust His heart," but this is truly where the rubber meets the road. You will not find comfort in choosing to trust God's heart if you do not have an accurate understanding of what is in His heart.

It is my hope that this book moves you closer to the Maker of the Universe, and I hope it gives you truth to hold on to as you walk this path that I am certain you did not want to travel. Whether you are just beginning this journey, have been traveling it for quite some time, or you have never personally walked this path for yourself but are keeping a friend company while they journey, I hope this book brings you encouragement to keep walking, keep trusting, and keep hoping.

It has been 12.5 years since I first began my battle with infertility. I now have four children, and the path toward desiring and conceiving each of them has looked vastly different. One friend lovingly said to me, "I think you can relate to all moms." She was referencing how each leg of my journey of parenthood could be its own stand-alone story.

I conceived my first child in 2005, 6 months after deciding I was ready to start a family. I naively expected to be pregnant the month following the decision to try, but in a relatively short time, I was joyfully expecting the start of motherhood. Little did I know, a little further down the road, in 2007, I would find myself begrudgingly initiated into the club called "Second Time Infertility." I longed for a second child for over a year, wondering why we were not able to conceive again, only to end up being referred to a fertility specialist. I experienced months and months of disappointment, diagnoses, discomfort (both physically and mentally) and medicine, but we were finally rewarded with the gift of another child after 2 years of longing and countless months of poking and prodding.

Enter the desire for child number three. Armed with the knowledge that conceiving again might be difficult, Todd (my husband) and I did nothing to prevent getting pregnant again. We knew we wanted another child, so after a year and a half of "wait and see," we sought refuge with our beloved fertility specialists again. We started right up where we left off with the advanced fertility treatments that had worked to get us pregnant with our second child, only to reach the end of the road and be told that our only option moving forward would be IVF. They gave us a .05% chance of being able to conceive on our own. Due to the cost and given that we expected our third child to be our last, we did not see IVF in our future; although, we continued to toss the idea around in the back of our minds.

After a total of four and a half years of desiring a third child including a whole year of failed (also expensive) fertility treatments, we decided to move forward being thankful for the two wonderful children we already had. We began dreaming and making plans for the future since we almost had the youngest in school. A full year after we finished our last fertility treatment, we sold all our baby gear (8 years of accumulating clothes, toys, you name it). Two months later we were shocked to find that with God a .05% chance is as good as 100%. We got pregnant with our third child. And when God does something, He does it completely. When He heals something, He heals it 100%. So when our third child was only 10 months old, and still being nursed, we got the biggest surprise of our lives. We were pregnant with a fourth child - a child that we had not even had time to stop and long for, but one that we received with open arms as a gift from heaven.

That's a quick peak at our story, minus the sordid details. I invite you to join me on the pages of this book as I take you deeper into our grief and anguish and deep wrestling with God. Through our 8+ year battle with infertility (and 14 year journey with parenthood), God has taught us invaluable lessons and strengthened us in ways we could not have imagined. I am excited to share those gifts with you.

The journey of desiring a child looks different for everyone. Whether you are reading this book because your life has personally been affected by infertility or the loss of a child, or you are keeping someone else company on their journey, I hope that this book ushers you to a place of hope and peace on an ill-defined, unpredictable path. If you are seeking healing for a mature heart that is past child-bearing years, but has not been able to stop aching for a child, I believe God has something for you on these pages as well. Allow me to walk alongside you for a little while.

Chapter 1

The Lonely Road

"Nobody knows...the trouble I've seen...
Nobody knows my sorrows."

"God is our refuge and strength, an ever-present help in trouble." [1]

There must be something in the water. I got tired of hearing this explanation for why there was a plethora of pregnant bellies sticking out everywhere I looked. I was drinking the same water, but I had no cute baby bump to show for it. It was ridiculous how many people were having children. When you are in your child-bearing years, you can expect to have pregnancies in your life. Naturally, some (okay, many) of your friends will be having babies. The Lord knows this was the case in my life, and I truly believe I was a part of the most fertile church in North America. When you mix together a congregation comprised of mostly people in their twenties and thirties and cold Michigan winters, you get babies cooking everywhere you look. Most couples were popping out a child every eighteen months to two years. The nursery at this church was bursting at the seams, and it did not look like the baby boom would be slowing down anytime soon. When I finally had my second child, no one from the church even knew to bring us a meal. There were that many babies. You did not get noticed for having one, and the sad reality was that everyone was too busy to notice if you were *not* having one. This was the environment I was surrounded with as I was on the lonely road of desiring a child. There were pregnant bellies everywhere I turned, and it did not seem like there were any people walking the same path as I.

I am going to assume you can understand where I am coming from. When you desire to become pregnant, it feels like everyone around you is pregnant or just had a baby. At one point, I made a list of every woman I knew who was in a position to have a child. I guess I wanted to prove that I was not crazy. I wanted to prove that I was the exception, that truly EVERYONE was getting pregnant. There were over 30 women on my list. (By the way, I do not recommend making a list – it only leads to despair as you realize that conceiving a baby is a lot easier for some than others.) The 30th person on my list got pregnant the month before we conceived our son, our 2nd born. If you do not have a list on paper, no doubt you have a list in your head. At every joyous announcement, a check mark is added to your fateful checklist that, when completed, means you are the last one picked for the team. When you are surrounded by Fertile Myrtles, desiring a child can feel very lonely.

God only knows.

Only God knows the timeline for when you will finally be able to hold a little miracle in your arms.

God usually keeps this timeline under wraps. There must be a reason. Could it be that if He answered our question, we might miss out on a valuable lesson? If we know when the journey is going to be over, we live differently. We live with the destination as the goal as opposed to living in the moment. If our focus is on the end, how often do we live and enjoy each day as a gift? Maybe you have heard the catch phrase, "Life is a journey, not a destination." It is catchy, but it is also true. Life is a journey with countless ups, downs, stops and changes in scenery. We can get tripped up when we become hyper-focused on any one thing.

Our curiosity about what comes next is exacerbated when things are tough. We think that if we know when the difficulty will end, somehow it will make the journey to get through the challenges easier. How long will I have to endure? Will this pain end in a positive outcome?

Unfortunately, having answers to these nagging questions turns our focus toward the destination (end result) as opposed to teaching us to follow the Guide. You see, if we think we know where we are going, there is no need to follow a guide. The problem is that only *the* Guide knows the best path to lead you through your troubles. When we take the lead, we tend to look for the most direct route from point A to point B, but we may be unaware of the pitfalls along our path. The Guide may take us a more roundabout way to our destination, but if we trust the Guide, we know that He is leading us down the best possible path for us.

A quick clarification: God is not leading you down the path of infertility. Infertility is NOT God's design or idea (more on this to come in later chapters). However, God is committed to leading you and walking alongside you as you walk through the brokenness of this world.

Okay, back to following the Guide: If you only call on God if you think you have gotten off track (blazing your own trail), there is little opportunity to build a relationship with Him. Your Maker wants to walk with you through this journey, reminding you that you are never truly alone. He wants to teach you how to place your hope in HIM, not in having a baby, or anything else for that matter. If you and I can learn how to keep our hope fixed on the One who never changes, we will never be disappointed.

> *"Hope deferred makes the heart sick,*
> *but a longing fulfilled is a tree of life."* [2]

If your hope is in anything other than God, you run the risk of your hope being deferred...postponed. If your hope is in anything other than God, there is no guarantee that fulfillment will come immediately, or ever.

Desiring pregnancy is the perfect example of a hope being postponed to the next month, and the next month, and... you get the point. The fulfillment of your deep desire gets pushed back to the next month, yet there is no guarantee that next month your desire will be fulfilled. Each time that your hope is deferred, discouragement can creep in.

Somehow the Holy Spirit kept Proverbs 13:12 on the forefront of my mind throughout my whole experience of desiring a second child. The majority of the time, I assumed the Lord was just trying to tell me that He understood – that my heart had a right to grow sick. It makes sense, right? I assumed the Lord was assuring me that it made sense to Him, too. My hope for a child kept getting deferred another month, so it was understandable, even expected, that I would be more and more depressed. However, the thing about God is that He does not look down from on high and see us in our pit of depression and say, *"Yeah, I see why you are in there. That is a bummer."* Instead, He is committed to removing us from our pits because He does not encourage pit dwelling. God had indeed kept this verse on my mind, but I did not get the message He was sending for quite some time.

My motivation to keep going was found in looking forward to the fulfillment of my desire and the promised "tree of life." I even spent hours trying to find baby names that meant "tree of life" or anything "tree" related. My focus was on what I wanted, not on the Giver. While I was waiting for my "tree" (the baby I was longing for), God was planting a more important seed and tending to it - a more significant tree that needed to be firmly rooted if I was ever going to truly enjoy the gifts He gives. That seed was a "longing for Him above everything else" seed.

A longing fulfilled is a tree of life. If we long for God above everything else, we will be filled. If God is our longing, the product will be life. If our hope is placed in other things, sooner or later we will be disappointed. It really is that simple. Hope planted in anything other than the desire for more of God will not grow into anything life-giving or life-sustaining. However, if your hope, the thing you look to for daily joy and fulfillment, is God and nothing material, you will not be shaken.

I can tell you that the seed God first planted in me years ago (the one where I learn to desire Him above any *thing*) has grown some roots and is now starting to take shape. He is faithful to continue the work He has started. My desire for God is growing, and I am learning how to have all of my desires flow through a heart that is first surrendered to Him. As the tree (desire for God) grows, it produces beauty and life-giving fruit which is a benefit to us and also provides us with something to offer others. It has been on this journey, on the road marked "infertility," that the Lord has done this good work in me, but it has been bumpy at times.

The Worst Weekend of my life

I will begin by sharing with you one particular weekend that I have deemed *the worst weekend of my life*. It began on a Friday morning when I awoke to find I had started my period. I was almost a full year into the pursuit of getting pregnant with baby #2. Starting your period when you really want to be pregnant is not a welcome event, not to mention the hormonal shifts that make you feel even worse about the whole ordeal. Shortly after this unwelcome news, I was given a familiar opportunity to die to myself (deny my feelings for the sake of someone else). My friend, Ela, called to tell me she was pregnant. It was another opportunity to master the art of rejoicing with those who are rejoicing. This, like the *many* opportunities before, was particularly difficult because it occurred during my fresh time of mourning the hope of being pregnant.

The plot thickens. Later that night, I went to see the movie Prince Caspian in which the very first scene is a woman giving birth. *Sweet, another reminder that I'm not pregnant,* I thought to myself. Saturday morning, I woke up to a phone call from my friend Katie. "Kel's in labor," she told me. I quickly got dressed and headed to the hospital to encourage and support Kelly and eagerly await the birth of her first child. Kelly and I, along with two other friends, Cari and Katie, used to get together on a weekly basis. These 3 were my support and encouragement, my closest friends. Cari happened to be in town from Kentucky, so our entire group was reunited for the day. As we sat there chatting during the progressing labor, I found myself trying not to think about my own predicament because I knew I would break down and cry. Somehow I managed to keep the following thought in my head, *This isn't the moment for me to feel bad for myself; I need to be a support for my friend.* I was doing fairly well sitting there with the three of them. I was trying not to think about the fact that Katie was a couple months pregnant, as we watched Kelly breathe through contractions. Then Cari dropped the bomb. She was pregnant with her third child, a surprise to her and her husband – a surprise that they welcomed, but not eagerly. They had been hoping to wait a year or so for another child. Suddenly, I was all alone, the only one of our group who was not pregnant – surrounded by the very birthing scene. Ugh!!!

Needless to say, it was a welcome distraction as Cari and I decided to leave the hospital for a couple hours (even though Kelly had not yet had her baby) in order to attend a wedding (the reason Cari was in town). To say I was struggling to think about anything other than how bad I was feeling about not being pregnant would be an understatement. I'm sure you have experienced something similar. When something is bringing you down, it seems like everything around you only adds to your sorrow. I was starving when we got to the wedding reception, since I had been at the hospital all day. When they sat my plate down in front of me, it was fish, sweet potatoes and green beans. The green beans did little to satisfy my hunger as I disliked fish and sweet potatoes. I wanted to weep into my plate of nastiness. The only thing that held me back was the knowledge that I would look ridiculous. No one would know that the real reason for my sorrow was not a meal I did not care for, it was the stress and fatigue of fighting a mental battle in which I was not feeling at all victorious.

Immediately after the meal, Cari and I knew we needed to hurry back to the hospital, hoping not to miss the birth. As we stood up to leave the table, the groom began speaking into the microphone. Eager to be somewhat alone, I wanted to get out of there as fast as I could. I was almost to the door when I heard, "Could we have every woman who is pregnant here stand up?" *What?!?!? Did he just say what I thought he said? Who does that at a wedding?* These were a few of the thoughts that flew through my mind. It was actually a very touching gesture on behalf of the bride and groom as they were giving their maid of honor a chance to announce her happy news. This just was not the day for me to be able to embrace such a nice gesture. *Seriously? Can this day get any worse?* I thought to myself. You have to know that as of today, I have been to well over 90 weddings and that was the ONLY wedding that an announcement like that has been made. It came at a very poignant time, don't you think?

So we drove back to the hospital that evening and waited for a couple hours, and finally Kelly's baby boy arrived. I headed home at around 1 a.m., exhausted on more than one level. The next morning, I was in much need of the encouragement I knew I would receive at church. The opening line of the sermon was, "We're pregnant." *We're pregnant?* I thought. *Who is pregnant? The church is pregnant? What?!?* The pastor went on to talk about how we as a church were going to "birth" a new church. I left there, probably looking shell-shocked, saying to the Lord, "*Seriously? I thought I'd be safe at church. I can't take any more.*"

That evening, my family and I stopped by the house of our closest family friends. These friends had battled infertility before conceiving their first child. I was able to unload the events of the weekend on them, finishing with the question I was sure was rhetorical, "So you're not pregnant are you?" My question hung in the air and I knew. Her face was a war of emotions, a twinge of a smile, but mostly sadness on my behalf. She was pregnant with a child that would be #3 in a short three years. They welcomed the pregnancy with open arms, but needless to say, they were hoping for some more space in between. What followed my question was one of a few times in my life that I can remember truly weeping in the presence of someone else. I wanted to run and hide and cry for days.

Five of my closest, dearest friends were pregnant at the same time. In one fell swoop, I was completely alone amongst every person I would turn to for comfort. It is in these moments – when you truly have nowhere else to turn – that you are primed and ready for the loving hand of your Maker. Here is a journal entry from that time in my life:

Well, it's unbelievable. I didn't think it could get any harder – but lo and behold, I found out that all of my closest friends who could be pregnant are all pregnant (or just had their baby). Finding out that Angie was pregnant felt like the straw that broke the camel's back, yet I'm not completely crippled. I feel crippled. I learned I have no refuge other than in you.

I learned that the only refuge I had was God.

What if the only refuge you have does not feel very comforting? I wanted a refuge other than the Lord. I wanted a tangible one, a refuge I could touch and talk to – not the one who communicates with me in my inner being. To communicate in that way is more difficult. It takes more intentionality, more quieting of the soul, more acceptance – all things I did not feel up for tackling.

Do you feel like a camel with a broken back (too many straws have piled up)- that somehow you are still walking around but you sense it is not a pretty picture to those around you? If so, you are not alone.

As long as there is someone or something to grab on to for strength or comfort, we grab. We choose the easiest route. Once all of our vices are taken from us, we realize that the things we were grabbing for were only temporary fixes.

They would not be able to offer a permanent solution. It is not wrong to lean on friends for comfort and support, but our friends and family were never meant to be a substitute for the real source of strength and comfort. God uses our friends and family to comfort us and minister to our hearts, but He did not intend for us to lean on people more than we would lean on Him. We can cry or complain or lament to friends, but ultimately they cannot do anything to change our situation, nor change our hearts. They can listen, but in the end our hearts need more than just a listening ear. Deep down, our hearts also need more than the knowledge that we are not the only one going through this difficult time. A hurting heart needs lasting comfort. A hurting heart needs solid guidance. A hurting heart needs unshakeable truth.

In one weekend, every person I would have leaned on for comfort was yanked from my hands. They were still there, but their presence caused an added struggle for me. They had what I wanted. I could not be around them without being reminded that I did not yet have a child. It was after this weekend that I began to see that ONLY God could be my refuge. It was time for me to pull up my bootstraps and learn just what it meant that the Lord is a refuge, a source of comfort. My depth of understanding was about to expand.

"God is our refuge and strength, an ever-present help in trouble."
(Psalm 46:1)

What does it mean to have God as our refuge?

A refuge, by definition is "a shelter or protection from danger or distress."[3] So God is our shelter and protection from danger or distress. Other dictionaries would use the word "hardships" in place of the word "distress." God is a place to go to find protection and safety from the hardships that plague us. You and I know how numerous the hardships are that plague the one who is desiring a child. This is where being able to grasp the concept of God as our refuge is so important.

If you have ever sat watching an outdoor sporting event, knowing that a violent storm was brewing and predicted to strike, you probably understand the importance of knowing where the closest shelter is. I can remember being at a horse show with a couple friends in mid August. As one friend was just about to head into the arena to compete we heard the siren scream, "Tornado Warning, Van Buren County." We were in a field in the middle of nowhere – the worst place to be in the event of a tornado. I remember thinking, *"Where do we go? Where do we go?"* I was panicked. I did not know where a safe place to find refuge would be – especially with a 1,000 pound animal in tow. We ran to the barn, where we thankfully had paid to rent a stall for the day, but as the rain and hail pummeled the ground outside and the sky was an ominous green, I did not feel safe. In a tornado, being under a roof does not guarantee safety.

The pain that results from our deep longing can feel like a 1,000 pound weight that prevents us from finding true shelter, true safety. We run to our "barns" which come in the form of family, or friends, or eating, or sleeping, or getting lost in television or shopping, but these "shelters" cannot protect you when the tornado of emotions hits on that first day of your period. If we have run to other things for shelter or refuge, we are not protected when we need it most. Just as I stood in that barn in the middle of nowhere, praying the tornado would not come our way, you and I have no way of knowing whether or not this month will be our last month of battling the disappointment. We have no way of knowing if we are in the path of the tornado. We need to be prepared. We *are* prepared if we are willing to take refuge in a sturdy shelter.

"Trust in him at all times, you people; pour out your hearts to him, for God is our refuge." (Psalm 62:8)

He is always there, inviting you to pour out your heart to Him. He does not expect you to walk the path without stumbling or without wanting to give up. He does, however, promise that He will help you, and He promises that with His help, we are guaranteed victory. So pour out your heart to Him. If you need help knowing what this looks like, check out David's words in Psalm 142:1-4:

"I cry aloud to the Lord; I lift up my voice to the Lord for mercy, I pour out before him my complaint; before him I tell my trouble. When my spirit grows faint within me, it is you who watch over my way. In the path where I walk people have hidden a snare for me. Look and see; there is no one at my right hand; no one is concerned for me. I have no refuge; no one cares for my life."

I take comfort in knowing that one of the "greats" of the Bible, the person known as "a man after God's own heart," struggled in much the same way we do. I feel like if David was a girl, I would wonder if he had battled infertility because it seems he has put our experience into words perfectly. *God, I feel totally alone. I don't like how things are going. You are the one who can do something about this, please have mercy. I have no where else to turn.*

The only wording of David's that I would change in order for it to be a perfect fit is this: I would change the words "people have" to "the enemy has" hidden a snare for me. The enemy of your soul has hidden a snare for you along this path. That snare is called isolation. He is trying to get you isolated so he can take you down and draw you away from any and all comfort, especially the Lord.

Isolation

During my season of infertility, as everyone around me was getting pregnant, I found myself reaching out and looking for those people who, like me, were desiring pregnancy but had not yet gotten pregnant. I wanted to gather every person around me who *was not* pregnant, so I could feel better about not being pregnant yet. The danger in doing this was that initially, I could gather quite a crowd around me, but one by one the members of my herd were getting picked off by the Shepherd and taken to a new herd, the one with all of the "expectant mothers." Their company was comforting for a season, but having their companionship for a while, only to have them "leave" my little circle of non-pregnant people, made it that much harder and that much more lonely when they left.

My road seemed especially lonely. I had a beautiful little girl toddling around when my battle with infertility began. We had no problem conceiving

Alliyah, so we were caught off guard when it became apparent that the road to bearing a second child might be a little (or a lot) more difficult. To those who had not yet been able to conceive a child, I feared that I appeared ungrateful or that my fears were stupid. "At least you know you are able to have a child," was the common remark I received. Their comments were really targeted at validating their own struggles, but, without realizing it, they were invalidating mine at the same time. Pain has a way of turning us inward, and we are often unaware of the effect we are having on others. While we are navel-gazing, we are missing out on what is going on in the lives of those around us. I did not have a single person in my life who had dealt with "second time infertility." I had never even heard the term.

I was alone.

Along comes the thought, *The Good Shepherd is the one snatching people from my non-pregnant herd. He is the Author of Life. Why isn't He "authoring life" in me?*

Isolation is the goal of the enemy of our souls. I felt utterly alone and Satan was working overtime to make sure that I would stay far away from the true source of Comfort.

A song comes to mind when I think about the trials that come with infertility. "Nobody knows the trouble I've seen. Nobody knows my sorrow." I have known the first two lines of this song for quite some time and I honestly thought it was Eeyore from Winnie the Pooh that coined the phrase. When I researched, I discovered that I was wrong and there was more to the song. The song continues, "Sometimes I'm up and sometimes I'm down. Oh yes, Lord. You know sometimes almost to the ground."

It is not clear who wrote this song, but it emerged from a time in history when our African-American brothers and sisters were being wrongly oppressed. They were treated as property rather than sons and daughters of the King. It was clearly written in response to the heart's cry, a way of dealing with the pain and suffering, for which there was no good explanation. Pain and suffering for which there was no GOOD explanation. Sound familiar? The singers of this song may not have been able to immediately change their situation, but their hope was that Someone saw their pain. Their pain did not go unnoticed.

Life bring ups and downs. No one can fully understand another's struggles, no one except Jesus. The writer of Proverbs (14:10) puts it this way.

> *"Each heart knows its own bitterness,*
> *and no one else can share its joy."*

No one can fully understand another's heart. I have a hard enough time trying to understand what is going on in my own heart let alone understanding the depths of another's. There is One who knows fully and understands fully. 1 John 3:20 says,

> *"We know that God is greater than our hearts,*
> *and he knows everything."*

Sometimes I'm up and sometimes I'm down.

My ups and downs looked very similar every month. After several days of being utterly depressed and feeling bad for myself, my hormones would level out and time made the initial shock less devastating. I would begin looking toward "trying again." This describes the beginning of the roller coaster of emotions.

A typical month in the life of the trying-to-conceive (TTC) begins low with a slow climb to the top until mid-cycle when you fly down the first of many hills with their highs and lows as you get excited at the hope that this month might be your last month on this journey and as you despair over every sign that points to the fact that this is probably not the month. The feelings that rage on the inside, while the rest of life is relatively normal, are enough to make any woman feel like she is going crazy. The rest of the world seems to be going about its business as usual and you are inwardly dying because the desire for a child grows with each passing day.

Maybe you are at a different place in your desire for a child. Maybe you have ridden the roller coaster only to be told you cannot conceive. Maybe you never had the chance to stand in line for the ride. Maybe your roller coaster has dipped so low that the ride was derailed through loss. If this is the case, I am truly sorry. Whatever your journey has looked like, one thing we all have in common is this:

The enemy of your soul, your oppressor, is working overtime to increase your pain, to keep you low, to isolate you, to numb your heart.

We can take this roller coaster analogy a little further. I remember being at an amusement park near closing time, and the ride attendants let us stay on the ride to keep riding as many times as we wanted as long as no one new was waiting to get on. Picture a teenager who has just ridden the same ride too many times to count. He has that look of, *I'm SO over this. This ride doesn't affect me anymore.* If you have been on the ride of infertility for very long, like the teenager, your heart begins to feel like, *"I'm SO over this."* If you are not careful, as a way of coping or self-protecting, your heart may grow numb and hardened. Knowing this is the case in many life scenarios, the writer of Proverbs warns, *"whoever hardens their heart falls into trouble"* (Proverbs 28:14).

If hardening your heart - choosing to stuff your emotions inside - is your way of dealing with pain, God warns you that you will fall into trouble. A hard heart cannot feel - it is numb. Numbness may feel helpful at the time, protecting us from the negative emotions, but our ability to feel happiness and joy is also dramatically affected. Throughout this book, I want to fight hard for your heart so that it does not grow numb – or more numb if you already feel numb. I want to remind you of truth so that you can keep your hope in Jesus, not in conceiving. I want you to know that you are not alone. I hope to equip you with the tools and skills to walk this path faithfully, skillfully, peacefully, and dare I say joyfully, for as long as you are called to walk this road. I know I want a lot, but I am not the only one who wants these things for you – your Maker wants them for you most of all. I know you want them, too.

Every story is different.

Your story is unique and I will not claim to understand everything you are going through, nor will I claim to have all the answers. Your pain is real. Your struggle is real. I will not deny you that for a second. I will, however, encourage you to cling to truth above your experience or circumstances. I will encourage you to pursue healing in the arms of Jesus. I will encourage you to fight for joy, a joy that transcends all other emotions and circumstances.

You are not alone. God is your refuge. He, and no other person, nor any other thing, is a true refuge. God is ever-present. He is always there. He never changes. He won't get pregnant. That's right. There is nothing about the nature of God that will make your pain any deeper or will cause you to struggle more than you are currently struggling. He is safe.

Notes:

---

1 Psalm 46:1

2 Proverbs 13:12

3 "Refuge." Merriam-Webster Dictionary. 5th. ed. Springfield, MA., 1997. Print.

Chapter 2

God, Why Aren't You Fixing This?

"Hope deferred makes the heart grow sick,
but a longing fulfilled is a tree of life."[1]

Questions

This chapter and the next are probably the most important chapters in the whole book. For a follower of Jesus, who desires a child, the heart of the struggle lies in this question for God: Why aren't You blessing us with a child? The deeper question that is woven into the fabric of this petition is: "Can I trust that your heart for me is good?" It is human nature to get mad at God and blame God when life circumstances do not work out the way we want. He is, after all, in control of all things, right? With infertility, the frustration is greater because He is the Author of Life. We wonder, *why isn't He "authoring" life in me?*

Our unanswered questions and struggles therein unmask us, leaving us vulnerable. Our emotions are raw and we are desperate to understand the heart of God. We teeter between doubting and hoping. We doubt God's goodness - that His heart is for our good. At the same time, we hope that we are wrong and that His heart is, in fact, good and that He will intercede on our behalf and stop the pain. Most of us swing back and forth on this pendulum of hope versus doubt all day long. In the midst of our swinging emotions and fluctuating affections for God, the constant feeling behind it all is vulnerability. Our deep desires are out there, exposed for all the world to see, and we do not know how God's "good plan" will unfold.

It is in the unknown and the uncertainty that we are most vulnerable. As a result, we often go into protective mode in which we harden our hearts a little bit so the pain and emotion are not so close to the surface. Unfortunately, the hard layer does not protect; it does the opposite. It causes us to die on the inside. Those of us with hard layers in our hearts go through the motions called life, but we are not fully alive. We are not totally free. The hard layer over my heart was my attempt at protecting the vulnerable part that so desperately wanted a baby. I did not want to expose the truly vulnerable area where the questions lingered: Is God for me or against me in my desire for a child? Do I want what He wants, or am I longing for something that He never intends to fulfill?

We can prevent these hard coatings from forming by understanding and remembering what God's heart really is. I have a good friend who has been nicknamed "Davidette" on a number of occasions. She is truly a woman after God's own heart and I believe she has a calling on her life to defend God's heart. It was invaluable to have her as a part of my life during my struggle to conceive a second child because she fought hard to help me trust God's heart when I wanted to doubt. She helped chisel away at those protective coatings. She upheld truth which caused my vision to come back into focus when it had been blurred by circumstances and I was no longer seeing God for who He really is. I had, unknowingly, chosen to let my experiences dictate what I believed about God as opposed to examining what I believed about God and allowing my experiences to flow from there.

Perspective

If our perspective of God is determined by how we feel or what we have experienced, we might have a very wrong understanding of who He is. Our emotions and how we feel about life at any given moment can change like the weather in Michigan. In one day, you can experience rain, then sun, then sleet, then hail, then sun again, and this all happens before breakfast. The running joke in Michigan is, "If you don't like the weather, wait five minutes and it will change." Is this what we want our affections toward God to be like? Wait five minutes and they will change? I like God right now. Things seem to be going well, but in five minutes it might be a different story. I might start my period.

Charles Swindoll put it this way, "life is really only about 10% what happens to you and 90% how you react to it."[2] If that is true, then 90% of our experiences in life are determined by how we choose to respond to the 10% of situations that are actually presented to us. That would mean that the majority of what we experience in life stems from our choices, not our circumstances.

It is as if we stand at a fork in the road every time we experience something circumstantially. If we respond to a situation poorly, our perspective about that situation will be marked by our poor response and we will begin traveling down one road. On the other hand, what if we choose the opposing response and are able to see clearly through our circumstance? The road we walk down following that encounter will look dramatically different.

Everyone has the opportunity to choose which path they will travel. Infertility is part of the 10%. You have no control over the fact that your life has been affected by infertility. You do, however, have control over how you will respond. You can choose the path that leads to bitterness or you can choose the more difficult path that clings to God's goodness above experience.

In order to respond well to life circumstances, we need clear vision. Our vision is warped if we are looking through negative lenses like fear, anxiety or despair. We simply do not see clearly when these emotions are present. In addition, we need to be careful to not let our beliefs (the way we see) be formed by our experiences. Rather, we will be well-served by clinging to truth until our experiences line up with what we believe. In order to not be completely knocked off our feet, we need to believe in something that is far more firmly rooted than our fickle emotions. We need to believe in truths that are true on good days and bad days and everything in between.

Trust Over Folly

The Word of God is the best place to park our beliefs because it has stood the test of time. The Bible is the most credible ancient book we have. It has been passed down from generation to generation and it holds encouragement for any life situation. It challenges us to grow, and guides us, showing us wisdom. The Bible is called the Word of God because it is his very words given to us, through men recording them, so that we may have access to encouragement from the very mouth of God whenever we need. The Bible teaches us about who this Maker of ours truly is, and it teaches us how to respond well to the circumstances we experience. The Bible has also revealed quite a bit about man as well. So before we look at who our Maker is, let's do some housekeeping at home. Proverbs 19:3 says,

"A person's own folly leads to their ruin, yet their heart rages against the Lord."

Can we agree that as humans we can sometimes get it wrong? Can we agree that it is possible for us to emerge from certain situations in our lives with a skewed view of God? It is human nature to get angry at God when life does not seem fair or situations turn sour, but our anger is not justified. Our anger at God is folly and will ultimately lead to our ruin. Our anger suggests that God has done something wrong. Our anger suggests pride - that we think we know better than God. We think that we would write a better story if we were in charge instead of Him. You might be thinking right now, *"I WOULD write a better story."* I know I have had that thought that on many occasions.

I realized it was silly of me to only know half the story but claim I could write a better one. It is only at the end of a story that you have the proper perspective to truly evaluate whether or not a story was good. I have witnessed the

Master Builder, the great I Am, carefully bring together all the shattered pieces of a person's life and create a beautiful masterpiece. I've seen it. I've experienced it. Sometimes we need to hold our horses and give God a chance to finish the story before we start to judge whether or not it is a good story. Yours is a good story. Hang tight as you watch each event unfold.

The story of Job offers us a lot to relate to when it comes to examining our own hearts and choosing to trust the heart of a good, loving, Father.

Before we really get into Job's story, there is a very important issue I want to clarify. When we look at the verse, *"A person's own folly leads to their ruin..."* I am not, for a second, suggesting that you are dealing with infertility because you have done something wrong. This is just not the case. Let me say that again. The fact that you are dealing with infertility is NOT because you've done something wrong. To suggest that your struggle is a result of your sin would be to jump on board with Job's friends. If you are not familiar with his story, allow me to quickly paint the picture found in the book of Job. Job was called, *"blameless and upright"* (Job 1:1). Satan complained to God concluding that the only reason Job loved God was because God had treated him well. Demonstrating that the enemy was wrong (and teaching us a powerful lesson), God allowed Satan to afflict Job in every way imaginable until Job was left with no tangible thing except the rotting flesh on his body. Job did not understand why his circumstances were so awful nor did anyone else in his life understand. The only explanation others could come up with to satisfy their answer to "why?" was to blame Job. (Maybe they were thinking of the verse about a person's own folly ruining his life...)

I don't want to be too quick to judge Job's friends. They were probably trying to understand what was going on so they could come up with a solution. They lectured Job, saying, "you must have done something wrong" - yet he had not. When he defended himself, his friends rebuked him for defending himself rather than defending God. In the end, God's response to Job's friends was, *"I am angry with you...because you have not spoken the truth about me, as my servant Job has"* (Job 42:7). Whoa! I have to know: What did Job say?

"I know that you can do all things; no plan of yours can be thwarted. You asked, 'Who is this that obscures my counsel without knowledge?' Surely I spoke of things I did not understand, things too wonderful for me to know...therefore, I despise myself and repent in dust and ashes" (Job 42:2-3,6).

Job lamented, but his faith remained in God. What was the lesson he learned? He recognized that God had a right to do anything with his life and he did not have a right to anything. Job understood that when life circumstances were going well, that was all grace. Although he was a blameless man, he knew he did not deserve a thing. If you are like me, you can tend to see God as a *cause-and-affect* manager of the blessings. If we are good, He blesses. If we are bad, He punishes. The story of Job and the life of Jesus tell us a different story. Our cause and affect beliefs about blessings are blown out of the water by Jesus's teachings. Jesus tells us to love our enemies and pray for them. He tells us to treat them differently than we think they deserve because that's what He does for us.

Job was on board with God's true managerial style: to love God and love people. It really is as simple as that. Jesus tells us to bless our enemies because that is the loving thing to do, even though it goes against our instinct. Job admitted that he lacked the understanding that God has; therefore, he admitted that God was more qualified to manage his life. He repented for the pride of thinking he deserved anything. He instead recognized that everything he had was a gift. Job was afflicted for a season and there was no good reason that anyone could name, yet we are told, *"The Lord blessed the latter part of Job's life more than the former part"* (Job 42:12). Like Job, we do not always understand the "why?" but in every bit of suffering, there is a promise of redemption.

We do not deserve anything, but the Father gives. We do not deserve a child, but the Father gives. We can not understand what is going on, but the Father's love persists.

If we do not get pregnant on our timeline, in our timeframe, our first inclination is to doubt God's heart. We doubt His goodness. We doubt His love. We think: *He must not want this for me.* This type of thinking is folly. On the other hand, if we dare to think God might want to give us a baby, then we are convinced that we need to fix something first, that somehow we must need to learn something or right some wrongs we've done. *Then God will bless me, right?* This line of thinking is also folly. God does want to bless you. He wants to bless you, but He does not want to bless you because you have done good things. His desire to bless is born out of His pure love for you, not out of what you have done. Look at Titus 3:4-5:

"At one time we too were foolish, disobedient, deceived and enslaved by all kinds of passions and pleasures. We lived in malice and envy, being hated and hating one another. But when the kindness and love of God our Savior appeared, he saved us, not because of righteous things we had done, but because of his mercy"

You may be asking, *If I don't have to fix something first, then why isn't He blessing me right now?* Many will try to comfort us, and we may even try to comfort ourselves with, "It's just not God's timing." As absolutely true as this statement is, it does little to satisfy the deeper question, "Will it ever be his timing?" Does God WANT me to have a child (or another child)? What is God's heart?

In order to understand God's heart, we do need to first address why all suffering (i.e. infertility) exists. As we do this, I will warn you - just as Job did not understand, you probably will not find an answer for why you, of all people, have to endure infertility. What we will examine is why God cannot just sweep in and immediately intervene on your behalf.

The Problem and the Solution

The problem is not with God. You see, there are two parties responsible for sin (suffering and separation from God) in this world. There are two parties responsible for the fact that you and I are dealing with the painful effects of sin existing in our world. Those parties are Satan and man. Satan brought the temptation to disobey God to Adam and Eve. He got them to believe that

God's heart was not good. Satan deceived Adam and Eve and got them to believe that God was in some way holding out on them. Have you ever felt this way? He turned our ancient mother's and father's eyes away from all that they had toward the one thing they could not have. As they stared at the forbidden tree, the longing grew until they could not contain it. They reached out, grabbed it, and ate the fruit. And we continue to eat the "fruit" of that decision today.

Can you relate to Adam and Eve? Are you longing for that one thing that seems out of reach? Have you found yourself so consumed with the one thing you cannot seem to have, that all the other blessings in your life have fallen by the wayside? The difference here is that the "tree" that you are longing for – that desire for a child - is not forbidden. It is woven into the very core and nature of the heart of God. God loves children. God loves life. He commanded Adam and Eve to "be fruitful and increase in number" (Genesis 1:28).

If God's heart is for us to be fruitful and have babies, why isn't He giving us a baby? My honest answer: I do not know. But hang with me, there is more to say. Isaiah 55:8-9 says,

"For my thoughts are not your thoughts, neither are your ways my ways, declares the Lord. As the heavens are higher than the earth, so are my ways higher than your ways and my thoughts than your thoughts"

1 Corinthians 2:11-12 says,

"For who among men knows the thoughts of a man except the man's spirit within him? In the same way no one knows the thoughts

of God except the Spirit of God. We have not received the spirit of the world but the Spirit who is from God, that we may understand what God has freely given us"

Who can discern the heart of God? His ways are higher than our ways. Here is what we *do* know. We live in a world tainted by sin. There are two guilty parties responsible for our tainted world: Satan and man. For God to remain 100% just, He would need to judge both parties who are responsible for the wrongdoing. Jesus offers a "not guilty" verdict to his beloved children, but God refuses to pass final judgment on this matter until the appointed time (we don't know when that is). The Bible teaches that God is waiting to pass final judgment until everyone hears the Good News and has an opportunity to choose or reject God (2 Peter 3:9). We do not know when that time is, although comically, many have tried to predict it. Just think about Y2K and even the Mayan calendar predicting the end of the world on December 21, 2012. We all long for the suffering to be over. We long to see justice for all the wrong in the world. In the meantime, man has free will and Satan also has *some* power to wreak havoc.

The fact that Satan has power would be a scary thought if our understanding stopped there. The only power Satan has is the power we give him. When Jesus died on the cross, He broke the power of the enemy forever, but he has not yet been banished to eternal damnation. In the time between the cross and final judgment, the enemy is parading around like he still has power until God's people stand against him. Satan cannot stand against those of us who have the very spirit of God living in us. According to Ephesians 1:13-14, that is everyone who believes in Jesus.

You see, God made a loophole in which He is able to act against Satan without simultaneously acting in judgment against man. The loophole's name is Jesus. Jesus limits the free-reign of the enemy. When Jesus, a sinless man, died on the cross, He received the wrath of all the sin of mankind. Since He put himself there willingly, though not deserving, He broke the power of evil (Satan). Therefore, when a follower of Jesus wields the name of Jesus, that person has the authority to stop the action of the enemy. God is able to act against one of the guilty parties (Satan) by using his children who are no longer guilty (through Jesus). When the sinless man, Jesus, died on the cross, He bought a "not guilty" verdict for any who would believe in Him and accept what He has done for them. God can use these redeemed followers of Jesus to oppose Satan without unjustly acting in judgment against Satan. We do not think it would be unjust for God to act against Satan because Satan is evil, but God cannot judge Satan without also judging man and punishing man for their equal share in the blame. Thanks be to Jesus who has rescued us from this punishment!!

2 Corinthians 1:21-22 puts this Good News in this way,

"Now it is God who makes both us and you stand firm in Christ. He anointed us, set his seal of ownership on us, and put his Spirit in our hearts as a deposit, guaranteeing what is to come."

As Jesus' people, we can stand firm in Christ, not fearing judgment. We can oppose the one who will be judged: Our enemy. We also have the Holy Spirit living in us, counseling us. I don't know about you, but I sure need his counsel.

The Counsel

Circumstances and beliefs do not always match up. For example, I think I'm a decent cook (at least my husband likes my cooking). If I happen to burn an item or the entire meal, does that mean I am not a good cook? No. I may have gotten distracted or the oven might have been malfunctioning. When our circumstances do not line up with what we believe, we experience a minor crisis, an opportunity to choose. We have to either choose to continue believing, regardless of what the circumstance says, or we doubt, which is unbelief. Some beliefs are more firmly rooted than others. Sometimes circumstances can pound on the side of our beliefs until finally we give in and the belief crumbles. That is why it is so important to be sure that what you are believing is rooted in something deep, something strong, something good. You may need to examine some of the things you believe about God, in order to see if they are rooted in truth or merely rooted in your circumstances.

It is a difficult, yet worthy, fight to stand and prevent our circumstances from dictating what we believe. If we listen to our circumstances, we hear a distorted truth (a.k.a. lies). We do this all the time. A guy rejects us in school and we receive, *Guys must not like me.* We don't get hired for a job and we consider, *Maybe I'm not cut out for this.* We make an unwise financial decision and we conclude, *I'm just not good with money.* We allow our circumstances to dictate what we believe and then we live our lives in response to those beliefs. When we do this, our circumstances continue to confirm these beliefs. The girl who was rejected walks around with low self-esteem, believing something about herself that just is not true. The unwise financial choice becomes a series of unwise choices. The rejected interviewee considers a new occupation instead of a different place of employment. When it comes to infertility, our experiences scream a lot of things at us, trying to get us to believe things that are not true.

Let's examine some of those distorted truths (lies) in the next chapter.

1 Proverbs 13:12

2 Charles R. Swindoll, "Charles R. Swindoll Quotes," *Thinkexist.com,* http://thinkexist.com/quotes/charles_r._swindoll/ (accessed January 3, 2013).

Chapter 3

God's Goodness vs. Distorted Truths

"I remain confident of this: I will see the goodness of the Lord in the land of the living." [1]

I'm not pregnant; therefore, God must not care, He must not hear, or I must not be asking right.

This was all I could say to make sense of my situation until the Lord opened my eyes to His truth. Let's break this statement down. With each claim, you have a choice. You can choose to believe what *feels* true right now, or you can choose to believe what *is* true always. In the season of infertility what *feels* true and what IS true often do not agree.

The feeling: *God must not care.* **The truth:** GOD CARES.

"Cast all your cares upon him, for he cares for you" (1 Peter 5:7).

HE CARES FOR YOU.

The feeling: *God must not hear.* **The Truth**: GOD HEARS.

"This is the confidence we have in approaching God: that if we ask anything according to his will, he hears us. And if we know that he hears us – whatever we ask – we know that we have what we asked of him" (1 John 5:14-15).

HE HEARS YOU.

The feeling: *I must not be asking right.* **The Truth:** GOD IS LISTENING.

"If my people, who are called by my name, will humble themselves and pray and seek my face and turn from their wicked ways, then will I hear from heaven and will forgive their sin and will heal their land" (2 Chronicles 7:14).

GOD RECEIVES ALL OUR REQUESTS, AND HE RESPONDS TO THE ATTITUDE OF OUR HEARTS, NOT THE WAY WE ASK.

It might not be God's will for me to have a child. How do I know it is God's will that I have a child?

Special privileges are included in your identity as a follower of Jesus. You are a child of the King (1 John 3:1). Yes, I am calling you a princess (or prince) because you are one. This very fact alone gives you many privileges. You have a right to anything in the Kingdom. As a daughter (or son) of THE KING, you are a rightful heir to anything in the kingdom. It is yours to possess. You do not need to ask for something as if you were an outsider. What I am describing here is the difference between a little girl who is at a friend's house asking for seconds at dinner. She asks and hopes, but is not sure that her request will be granted. The daughter of the family asks for seconds at the same meal and she fully expects that her request will be granted. She knows her parents' hearts. She knows the rules of the family. She does not expect to be turned down.

If you are a daughter of the King, you should not expect to be turned down if you are asking for something of the kingdom of heaven. There is no right or wrong way to ask for a child. If you ask according to his will, you know he has heard, and you know you have what you asked for.

I can hear your questions now: *Well, how do I know it is God's will that I have a child? If I have what I've asked for, why don't I have what I have asked for?* These are valid questions. I have asked them myself. *Is asking for a child asking for something that is of the kingdom of heaven?* YES! But don't just take my word for it. Search the Bible for yourself.

"Has not the Lord made them one? In flesh and spirit they are his. And why one? Because he was seeking godly offspring" (Malachi 2:15).

"For no matter how many promises God has made, they are "Yes" in Christ. And so through him the "Amen" is spoken by us to the glory of God" (2 Corinthians 1:20).

God is seeking godly offspring, as in, offspring from people who will raise their children to know Him. Thanks to Jesus, the answer to every question that aligns with a promise God has made is, "yes." Has God promised fertility? Yes!! Here is the proof:

Every woman in the Bible who is barren and asks God for a child is healed and receives a child. EVERY woman. Here is a brief look into their stories.

Sarah - who receives Isaac

In Genesis 17:15-17 we read, God said to Abraham, *"As for Sarai your wife, you are no longer to call her Sarai; her name will be Sarah. I will bless her and will surely give you a son by her. I will bless her so that she will be the mother of nations; kings of peoples will come from her.'*

Abraham fell facedown; he laughed and said to himself, 'Will a son be born to a man a hundred years old? Will Sarah bear a child at the age of ninety?'"

You can read more of Sarah's story in Genesis 16-22.

Rebekah - who receives Jacob & Esau, twins

Rebekah is Abraham's daughter-in-law. Did infertility run in the family? It didn't matter for Rebekah and it doesn't matter if infertility runs in your family either.

In Genesis 25:19-21 we read, *"This is the account of Abraham's son Isaac. Abraham became the father of Isaac, and Isaac was forty years old when he married Rebekah...Isaac prayed to the Lord on behalf of his wife, because she was barren. The Lord answered his prayer, and his wife Rebekah became pregnant."*

You can read more of Rebekah and the twins' story in Genesis 25:19-34.

Manoah's Wife - who receives Samson

We don't know her name, but we know her story.

In Judges 13:2-5 we read, *"A certain man of Zorah, named Manoah, from the clan of the Danites, had a wife who was sterile and remained childless. The angel of the Lord appeared to her and said, 'You are sterile and childless, but you are going to conceive and have a son. Now see to it that you drink no wine or other fermented drink and that you do not eat anything unclean, because you will conceive and give birth to a son. No razor may be used on his head, because the boy is to be a Nazirite, set apart to God from birth, and he will begin the deliverance of Israel from the hand of the Philistines.'"*

You can read their story in Judges 13.

Hannah - who receives Samuel

Hannah knows what it is like to be tortured both by an inward desire and by the people surrounding her.

In 1 Samuel 1 we read that there was a man named Elkanah who had two wives. One was Peninnah (fertile myrtle) and the other was Hannah who had no children. Once a year, they would all go to Shiloh to worship the Lord. Here is the account from verses 4-11:

"Whenever the day came for Elkanah to sacrifice, he would give portions of the meat to his wife Peninnah and to all her sons and daughters. But to Hannah

he gave a double portion because he loved her, and the Lord had closed her womb. And because the Lord had closed her womb, her rival kept provoking her in order to irritate her. This went on year after year. Whenever Hannah went up to the house of the Lord, her rival provoked her till she wept and would not eat. Elkanah her husband would say to her, 'Hannah, why are you weeping? Why don't you eat? Why are you downhearted? Don't I mean more to you than ten sons?'

Once when they had finished eating and drinking in Shiloh, Hannah stood up. Now Eli the priest was sitting on a chair by the doorpost of the Lord's temple. In bitterness of soul Hannah wept much and prayed to the Lord. She made a vow, saying, 'O Lord Almighty, if you will only look upon your servant's misery and remember me, and not forget your servant but give her a son, then I will give him to the Lord for all the days of his life, and no razor will ever be used on his head.'"

If you read further, you learn that Eli observed Hannah and thought she was drunk because of the rawness and realness from which she poured out her soul to God. When he realized she was not drunk, he blessed her and told her that she would have what she asked for (1 Samuel 1:12-17). The next morning they worshipped and headed home and then we read in verses 19-20, *"Elkanah lay with Hannah his wife, and the Lord remembered her. So in the course of time Hannah conceived and gave birth to a son. She named him Samuel, saying, 'Because I asked the Lord for him.'"*

Both the 1st & 2nd books of Samuel are dedicated to a continuation of their story if you are curious.

Elizabeth - who receives John the Baptist

We read about Zechariah and Elizabeth in Luke 1:6-7, *"Both of them were upright in the sight of God, observing all the Lord's commandments and regulations blamelessly. But they had no children, because Elizabeth was barren; and they were both well along in years."* Their story goes like this: an angel visits Zechariah when he is worshipping the Lord and the angel tells him that his prayers have been heard and his wife, Elizabeth, will give birth to a son, and the angel says,[2] *"and you are to give him the name John. He will be a joy and a delight to you, and many will rejoice because of his birth, for he will be great in the sight of the Lord"* (Luke 1:13-15).

You can read their full story in Luke 1:5-25.

Here's the part I love about what you have just read: Every child who was given as a gift after a long season of barrenness was a great part of God's plan. Isaac, Jacob (and Esau), Samson, Samuel, John the Baptist....those are some powerful men. Those are most of the "greats" of the Bible, and they all came from women who were barren for a long time.

I wonder what plans God has in store for your child(ren)...

Now, I want to be honest with you. I found one woman in the Bible that we are told did not have children. She was Michal, David's wife. God has carefully selected the stories He would give us in the Bible to learn from. He has overwhelmingly shown us that EVERY woman who was barren AND asked for a child, was given one – and all of these children were children of the prom-ise. They were children that God would use to fulfill His great plan for re-demption. We are children of the promise, and He wants to use our offspring to fulfill His plans for redemption as well. This is still true, even in light of Michal's story. So let's look at Michal's story and we will see why the Bible says she had no children.

Michal

2 Samuel 6:14-16, 20-23 says, *"David, wearing a linen ephod, danced before the Lord with all his might, while he and the entire house of Israel brought up the ark of the Lord with shouts and the sound of trumpets. As the ark of the Lord was entering the City of David, Michal daughter of Saul watched from a win-dow. And when she saw King David leaping and dancing before the Lord, she despised him in her heart...When David returned home to bless his household, Michal daughter of Saul came out to meet him and said, 'How the king of Israel has distinguished himself today, disrobing in the sight of the slave girls of his ser-vants as any vulgar fellow would!' David said to Michal, 'It was before the Lord, who chose me rather than your father or anyone from his house when he appointed me ruler over the Lord's people Israel – I will celebrate before the Lord. I will become even more humiliated in my own eyes. But by these slave girls you spoke of, I will be held in honor.' And Michal daughter of Saul had no children to the day of her death."*

Michal did not have any children because God had not chosen Saul's family to continue the throne – to be the line that the Messiah would come from. If you remember Saul's story, God only allowed him to sit on the throne as king because the people of Israel chose him. The people wrongly saw his outward appearance and thought he was the best candidate. But God knew Saul's heart and allowed the people to make their choice, but it was not ultimately what He wanted. God allows free will, but He will ultimately work out His purposes. Once Saul died, God was able to raise up David, His chosen one. This interaction between Michal and David reveals what was in Michal's heart. She did not honor God's chosen one, even though he was her husband. As a result, God's hands were tied. He could not bless her with children. She could not receive the blessing of a legacy because the legacy she would leave would not bring honor to God. She did not get on board with God's plan. The Bible even says that David was coming home to *bless* his family. Michal greeted David at the door with her contempt for what she had just seen instead of welcoming David AND *the blessing* that he would bring. Later, Michal's father gave her to a different man to be his wife.

As Jesus' followers, we are God's chosen. If you are a follower of Jesus, you do not need to worry whether or not God would chose to bless you with a child. You are a daughter of the King of kings. He has already chosen you. Here is the proof from God's word:

Ephesians 1:11-14 says, *"In him (Christ) we were also chosen, having been predestined according to the plan of him who works out everything in conformity with the purpose of his will, in order that we, who were the first to hope in Christ, might be for the praise of his glory. And you also were included in Christ when you heard the word of truth, the gospel of your salvation. Having believed, you were marked in him with a seal, the promised Holy Spirit, who is a deposit guaranteeing our inheritance until the redemption of those who are God's possession – to the praise of his glory."*

"How great is the love the Father has lavished on us that we should be called children of God. And that is what we are!" (1 John 3:1).

"Now if we are children, then we are heirs – heirs of God and co-heirs with Christ, if indeed we share in his sufferings in order that we may also share in his glory" (Romans 8:17).

Kingdom Benefits

If you follow Jesus, you have been included with Christ. You are a co-heir with Christ of the kingdom of God and all the benefits that come with it. What comes with it? Before we can address that, we need to understand what the kingdom of heaven means. Talk of "kingdom" stuff used to be lost on me because, as an American, I do not live in a "kingdom" society. I did not understand what it meant to pray for "the kingdom of God" to come. Here is what I have come to understand. When we pray for the kingdom of God to come, we are praying that the borders of the kingdom of heaven be ever increasing until the whole world is being ruled by heaven. Currently, there are far too many places in the world that are being ruled by, and are under the oppression of, the kingdom of darkness. That simply means that evil is prevailing and we need the kingdom of heaven to extend its borders into those places so that the evil and malpractices that are taking place can no longer occur.

Spiritually speaking, the whole earth belongs to the Lord, but there are areas that are not under the rulership of the kingdom of heaven. These areas are being run by the kingdom of darkness, and it is our job, as sons and daughters of the King, to take that territory back so it belongs to its rightful owner: God. Jesus brought the kingdom of God to earth because He is a permanent resident in heaven. When Jesus left earth and went back to Heaven, He sent the Holy Spirit to live in His followers – thus, making more residents of heaven.

When the kingdom of God collides with the kingdom of darkness, the kingdom of God overcomes. Every. Time. The kingdom of God brings restoration and healing. Jesus taught us to pray for God's will to be done "*on earth **as it is** in heaven*" (Matthew 6:10, emphasis added). In other words, He taught us to pray that the earth would come under the rulership of heaven. The rules of heaven are love, joy, peace, etc.

You are chosen. God's heart is for you, not against you – because of Jesus. When Jesus hung on that cross, He accomplished so much. He saved us from death. That does not mean that He bought our forgiveness so we could just squeak by and not have to go to hell. He saved us from death, all death.

Infertility is death. Infertility is not life, it is the opposite. It is the death of a dream. It is a womb that was meant to bring forth life that is not producing life. If something is not producing life, we call it dead. That is why what Jesus did on the cross is such good news!

Isaiah 53:5 says, *"He was pierced for our transgressions, he was crushed for our iniquities; the punishment that brought us peace was upon him, and by his wounds we are healed."*

By His wounds, we are healed. Jesus was wounded and died to break the curse of death. Death no longer has mastery over him, or us, because we are His. Remember, we are co-heirs with Him. In Christ, we were healed completely: mind, body, spirit. We were made whole. Completely. That means no barrenness.

One More Question: *If I have what I've asked for, why don't I have what I've asked for?*

If Christ has already accomplished my healing, declaring me fertile, why am I still childless?

Sometimes we have to wait for the tangible.

Remember: *"This is the confidence we have in approaching God: that if we ask anything according to his will, he hears us. And if we know that he hears us – whatever we ask – we know that we have what we asked of him"* (1 John 5:14-15).

When we pray, things change in the unseen, spiritual realm. We cannot always see the effects of these changes right away, but our prayers change things.

We have to trust that our prayers change things because Jesus encouraged us to pray. He himself prayed. The fact that healing may not come instantaneously does not mean that it is not God's will to heal. We do not understand the intricacies of how everything fits together. When our circumstances (we are still childless) do not line up with what we believe (God's heart is pro-children, anti-barrenness), we have to choose to hold tighter to our beliefs until our beliefs transform our circumstances.

We want it to be his time now. I think God gave us examples like Sarah, Rebekah, Manoah's wife, Hannah and Elizabeth so we would feel better about having to wait a couple months or a couple years, as opposed to decades like they did. Their stories also give us hope that the Lord has something powerful planned for the children He has planned for us.

"Hope deferred makes the heart grow sick, but a longing fulfilled is a tree of life." (Prov. 13:12). There were two trees that stood side by side in the Garden of Eden. One was called "the tree of life," and the other was called, "the tree of the knowledge of good and evil."[3] Once Adam and Eve ate from the tree of the knowledge of good and evil, they were no longer permitted to eat from the tree of life. God closed off their access to that tree by banishing them from the Garden.[4] When we choose to want God more than any other thing, He grants us access to the tree of life. He *is* the Tree of Life. He is the one who has made us to live forever. When we have access to Him, our life is good, fruitful, and "pleasing to the eye." On the other hand, when try to find nourishment and fulfillment in anything other than the Tree of Life, our lives

look more like the picture of a camel walking around with a broken back. Without proper nourishment, we falter under the weight of life.

Maybe you have not hit your breaking point yet. Maybe the final straw has not been placed on your back, but a weighed down camel is still pretty silly looking. You were not meant to walk around with heavy weights. That is why Jesus said, *"Come to me, all you who are weary and burdened, and I will give you rest. Take my yoke upon you and learn from me, for I am gentle and humble in heart, and you will find rest for your souls. For my yoke is easy and my burden is light"* (Matthew 11:28-30).

He says to us (fill your name in the blank), "Choose to follow me, _____, and learn from me, _____. I am gentle and humble in heart and you, _____, will find rest for your soul."

You may not be able to answer the question, *"God, why aren't you authoring life in me now?"* But you can trust the Holy Spirit, who lives in you if you are a follower of Jesus, to remind you of the heart of God, so you can believe and not doubt. Your only Refuge is not a good refuge if you cannot trust His heart.

Do you believe He is good? No matter how your story unfolds, will you choose to believe that God is good? Even though we can see clearly in scripture that God is pro-fertility, if you never receive a child from your womb, will you still believe He is good? It is a sobering question, but an honest answer is the key to unlocking greater freedom as you learn to trust the Author of your story. He is either good all the time or He is not good at all. You will never go wrong trusting in God's goodness regardless of whatever feelings come your way through circumstances.

His heart is **not** pro-barrenness. His heart is pro-fertility. Read that again slowly and trust.

Psalm 113:9 declares, *"He settles the barren woman in her home as a happy mother of children."*

This is your promise. This is your future. This is God's heart for you. Will you trust His goodness and embrace the unique story He is writing for YOU?

Notes:

––––––––––––––––

1 Psalm 27:13

2 Summary of verses in Luke 1:11-13.

3 Found in Genesis 2:9.

4 Summary of Genesis 3:22-24.

Chapter 4

Wired to Be a Mom

"So God created man in his own image, in the image of God he created him; male and female he created them. God blessed them and said to them, 'Be fruitful and increase in number; fill the earth and subdue it.'"[1]

Life

God was and is the first pro-lifer. If He drove a car, He would definitely have a bumper sticker that says, "Pro Life." Unlike those we see on the bumpers of cars, His sticker would not refer to a stance on abortion. His sticker would simply be a proclamation of what He stands for: LIFE.

He is the giver of life. He is the Author of life. All life originates with Him. We were made to be like Him.

In the first chapter of Genesis, we read the account of how God created the earth and everything in it, including mankind. On the sixth day, we are told that God created man and woman in His image. The fact that we are made in the image of God is both complex and simple. It is complex because it is not possible for man to fully understand all that God is: His character, His nature, how He thinks and acts. Without a clear understanding of the One we are made to be like, we can not fully know what it means to be made like Him. On the other hand, some things about God are simple and clear, giving us a glimpse of what it means to be made like Him. Through the Word of God, we have the opportunity to learn a lot about the God of the Universe. The very first thing we learn about Him is that He is the Creator.

In Genesis 2:4-7 we read: *"This is the account of the heavens and the earth when they were created, when God made the earth and the heavens. Now no shrub had yet appeared on the earth and no plant had yet sprung up, for the Lord God had not sent rain on the earth and there was no one to work the ground, but streams came up from the earth and watered the whole surface of the ground. Then the Lord God formed a man from the dust of the ground and breathed into his nostrils the breath of life, and the man became a living being."*

Seeds and Trees

I am excited about what I am about to share with you. I went looking in Genesis in order to find the verse about us being made in the image of God. I found that passage and, oh, did God open my eyes in a whole new way. Listen to this: When God made the earth, no plants had "appeared" yet. In other words, when God created everything, the plants that He created were just seeds. They were ready to spring up and become something living, but they needed the water that God would send. They were created, yet they had not yet fully become all that they were intended to be. He did not create the full-grown plant. He created the seed. To become all they needed to be, they needed rain, and something else.

Why didn't God create the mature plants from the beginning? The answer is in the passage: *"There was no man to work the ground."* From the very beginning, God intended for mankind to take part in the act of creating. God made us like Him (creators) and He gave mankind an opportunity to put that nature into practice from the moment He gave man breath.

As women, we are made as equally in the image of God as men, but one of our roles as "creators" is unique. When He made women, He gave us the special privilege of being the "soil" that the seed was planted in, waiting to spring to life. When we were still in our mothers' womb, we had all our "seeds" of life in us. In utero, we had every egg that we would ever have. Men, on the other hand, do not develop the ability to help those seeds grow until they are older. God has entrusted us with the seeds from the very beginning of our lives. Is it any wonder that motherhood is so deeply rooted in us? This is why you are not satisfied in your barrenness. Barrenness means nothing is growing - which is the opposite of what the kingdom of God is about. Allow me to say it again: The kingdom of God is about LIFE.

Look at how God carefully nurtured the first life He had created as we continue in the passage in Genesis 2:8-9 & 15-17:

"Now the Lord God had planted a garden in the east, in Eden; and there he put the man he had formed. The Lord God made all kinds of trees grow out of

the ground – trees that were pleasing to the eye and good for food. In the middle
of the garden were the tree of life and the tree of the knowledge of good and evil...

...The Lord God took the man and put him in the Garden of Eden to work it
and take care of it. And the Lord God commanded the man, 'You are free to eat
from any tree in the garden; but you must not eat from the tree of the knowledge
of good and evil, for when you eat from it you will certainly die.'"

God had already prepared a garden for Adam, even though we were just
told that elsewhere in the world, God had only planted seeds. God had a
whole "nursery" prepared for His firstborn. And like a good parent, He provided everything that His son would need to live. True to the nature of being a
good parent, He also gave His child freedom, with some guidance. In the
middle of the garden was the tree of "LIFE" as well as a tree that provided the
choice of whether or not to obey God. We have all wished that the choice had
never been given. We wish that sin was not allowed to reign in this world. The
effects of sin are devastating. Infertility is a product of living in a world that
has not yet been fully redeemed from the brokenness that entered through
Adam and Eve.

The Seed of Doubt

Since the very beginning, when God chose women to be the bearers of life,
that life-giving nature has been under attack. Let's look at how this unfortunate fate fell upon us. In Genesis 3, Adam and Eve are deceived by the enemy.
Their hearts are turned toward the one thing they can not have and suddenly,

for the first time in their existence, they feel as though they are missing something.

"Did God really say, "You must not eat from any tree in the garden?" the enemy jeers. The enemy thinks: *Can I get her to doubt God's goodness? Can I get her to think God is holding out on her?*

"We may eat fruit from the trees in the garden, but God did say, 'You must not eat fruit from the tree that is in the middle of the garden, and you must not touch it, or you will die,'" Eve responds.[2]

She answers according to her recollection of what God had said, but the seed of doubt was planted simply by being asked the question. We do not know how long Adam and Eve lived in the garden before the serpent came with this tempting question. We are also uncertain as to how much time had passed since God had given them the command. What we do know is that up until that moment in history, Eve had no reason to doubt the goodness of God. Her trust in God was complete and pure. All it took was a simple question (a seed) to knock Eve off course. Suddenly all the fullness that she had been experiencing seemed a little incomplete. The seed of doubt had been planted. As we will see, even a tiny seed can accomplish a lot.

No matter the size of doubt we are wrestling with, the presence of doubt can obscure our memory. Eve's response was almost accurate but she added a little something of her own. You see, God never said anything about dying if you *touch* the tree of life. He said that they would die if they ate from it. I wonder if Eve added that little tidbit because until the seed of doubt had been planted, she never had a desire to even touch the tree. Due to the fact that Adam and Eve were not allowed to eat from the tree, what use was there in touching it? At the moment that the seed of doubt was planted, a desire was planted, too. I like to give Eve the benefit of the doubt and think that she could feel the desire growing, and so she reasoned that she must not go near that tree or she may give in to the desire to do the very thing God had forbidden. Even if we could credit Eve with such wisdom, the unfortunate reality remains. She went and she ate.

Having "wants" and "desires" without the assurance of fulfillment is the reality in which we find ourselves living today, but that was not the original design. Can you wrap your mind around having a want or desire that was 100% pure? Can you fathom what it would be like to have wants and desires without even a thread of doubt that those wants and desires would be fulfilled? This was the environment Adam and Eve were given. I am sure the majority of their time was spent learning their surroundings and standing constantly in awe of all that God had made and his gracious, loving care. It would seem that if they had a desire, it was fulfilled: *I am hungry. I want something to eat.* Pick and eat. *I want to explore that.* Go and explore. *I want to see what that animal feels like.* Go and touch. There were no limitations except the one that God had laid out in His first instructions. Every other desire could be fulfilled instantly. We do not read that Adam and Eve ever struggled with the desire to touch the one thing they could not have. I imagine that this is because every other desire of theirs could be fulfilled instantly. Why dwell on the one thing they could not have?

Wouldn't it be nice if we could be thankful for all that we do have, rather than focus on the one thing we do not have? More on this in Chapter 7, but for now, let's look at why this is so hard to do. James 1:13-15 says,

"When tempted, no one should say, 'God is tempting me.' For God cannot be tempted by evil, nor does he tempt anyone; but each one is tempted when, by his own evil desire, he is dragged away and enticed. Then, after desire has conceived, it gives birth to sin; and sin, when it is full-grown, gives birth to death."

The first evil desire to ever exist was the desire to eat the forbidden fruit. Every other desire that Adam or Eve had up until that point, I imagine, were fulfilled instantly because their desires were good and pure. Then the tempter came and offered a new kind of desire. From there, Adam and Eve were dragged away and enticed by their own evil desire. That desire grew into an action, and the rest is history. Death entered our world carrying all its baggage in its various forms. The form you and I are wrestling with is infertility.

Before we continue, I want to be sure to make one thing clear: Your desire to have children is a good desire. Maybe I did not need to say it, but I will say it again because truth is always good to hear. Your desire to have children is a good and right thing. I do not know your reasoning for wanting to have children, but the simple desire to have children is beautiful, pure, and of God.

Digging Up the Bad Seeds

Let's get back to Adam and Eve's story in order to gain greater insight into our own stories. Adam and Eve had the privilege of living an existence that did not include doubt. Once again, if they had a desire, there was no doubt that it would be fulfilled. They did not seem troubled by the fact that there was a tree they could not eat from until the serpent planted a seed of doubt about God. Remember, the seed came in the form of a mere question. Did God really say...? Until then, they trusted God completely. If He said "Do," they did. If He said, "Don't," they didn't, and there was no question asked and no burden felt.

Trust is like that. The lack of trust (*a.k.a. doubt*) begins with a suggestion and grows into a monstrous burden if that suggestion is not replaced with truth. Do you doubt your suitability as a mother? Has the suggestion that *maybe you haven't gotten pregnant yet because you wouldn't be a good mom* crossed your mind? Do you believe you are faulty or broken because you haven't been able to bear life in your womb?

Try not to let those questions trip you up. I want to expose the hidden attack that lies beneath the surface of those questions that we wrestle with. Since sin entered the world, the enemy of our souls has been going after who we are as women, particularly as life-givers, as mothers.

Do you remember when that first seed of doubt, about who you are as a mother, was planted in you? That simple question of, "Am I going to be able to get pregnant?" could have been born out of the tiniest situation. Maybe a relative asked you when you and your husband were going to have children. Maybe you watched a mother in the store and wondered if you would do things differently *some day*. Maybe the doctors diagnosed you as a teen and you have since lived with the fear that you would not be able to have children. Maybe for you it took a friend talking about adoption for that first ping of fear to grip you and cause you to wonder if you would be able to carry a child in your womb.

If there was an initial seed of doubt planted in you, it may have grown some roots by now. Ironically, the water source that gives viability to those roots usually comes in the form of more questions and more suggestions that God is not good or that we are not fit to be mothers. The more questions or suggestions that come, the more we doubt and the bigger our "plant" of doubt, unbelief and despair grows. As the cycle of doubt continues, what was once a tiny seed becomes a tree that grows right in front of our eyes and prevents us from clearly seeing our situation for what it is: A painful path we are walking that is a result of our broken world. I have never had the desire to go near a chainsaw, but, sister, I would gladly wield one against the trees of doubt and mistrust that plague us in this area. Let's hack at the trees of doubt that may be obscuring your view of motherhood. Shall we?

We were meant to bring forth life - at the core of who we are.

Look at the consequence of that one single act of distrust: *"To the woman he said, 'I will greatly increase your pains in childbearing; with pain you will give birth to children'"* (Genesis 3:16).

The very first thing that God addresses, as He explains the consequence of her choice not to trust, is her childbearing. This is the thing that is most deeply rooted in who she is and who she was made to be. She was made to be a bearer of life. Her distrust in God meant that there would be turmoil with the thing she was made to do. God did not want the turmoil for her. He is just spelling out the consequences of her choice to not trust Him. You are Eve's daughter - therefore, the thing that is most deeply rooted in what you were made to do is also under attack. Thankfully, that is not the end of the story. Jesus' death broke the curse of the law of sin and death. Romans 8:1-2 says:

"Therefore, there is now no condemnation for those who are in Christ Jesus, because through Christ Jesus the law of the Spirit who gives LIFE <u>has set you free</u> from the law of sin and death" (emphasis added).

Since we have been declared not guilty of sin, by the atonement of Jesus, we no longer need to bear the consequences of that original sin. When Jesus died, His death provided the ability to restore everything to the way it was meant to be in the beginning - before sin. Jesus' death accomplished what we could not do on our own. He reversed the power of hell. The power that the enemy had is no longer, but our enemy does not want his opponents (us) to know that his power is limited. If his opponents (we) knew that his power was limited, the match would be won. Thus, our enemy goes after our hearts. He goes after what we believe about God, the One who was and is powerful enough to defeat him. If Satan can get us to doubt God, he can render us incapable of creating any real opposition, and then he can have his destructive way in our lives. He goes after the things that will affect our hearts deepest at the core because it is there that we are most vulnerable. A good fighter learns the weakness of their opponent and goes after that spot. Our enemy is crafty and he knows that going after the very thing we were made to do (bear life) will have the greatest impact.

But let's not dwell on the battle. Let's celebrate the victory we have. Do you still need further convincing that you have been declared whole again by Jesus? We are told in John 10:10, that Jesus came that we *"may have life, and have it to the full."* Jesus restored us so that we might have a full life. Proverbs 30:15-16 puts it this way:

"There are three things that are never satisfied, four that never say, 'Enough!': the grave, the barren womb, land, which is never satisfied with water, and fire which never says, 'Enough!'"

An empty womb is just that: It is empty! It is the opposite of full. The barren womb is never satisfied. The barren womb is not a full life. Barrenness is death. God did not intend for the womb to be barren. It is not God's heart that we be barren. It is okay that you are not satisfied with your barren womb. Your Maker agrees.

Before we go any further, I want to speak to the heart that is "well advanced in her years" or for some medical reason will not have the privilege of carrying a child in her womb. With an extreme amount of love, I say to you: What you have experienced is NOT what God intended from the beginning. In a sin-free world, you would not have had to walk the path that you have walked. If you desired to carry a child in your womb and were unable to, I am so sorry. The fact that you have not been able to carry a child in your womb, does not mean that you have been denied the opportunity to mother – which is a jewel that is set deeper and more securely in the core of who you are than the physical act of carrying a child. Maybe you have chosen to adopt or maybe you have chosen not to expand your family. Whatever your choices, your story is beautiful, and I guarantee God has been at work to bring about the best possible good. I am confident that you have still been presented with opportunities to mother, and I guarantee that you will have many opportunities presented in the path ahead of you. Mothering is more than who you are; it is what you do, too.

On the day I was writing this, I shared with a fifty-something year old friend that I was writing this book. As we discussed this topic of motherhood, I watched as my friend was moved to tears as she explained that she had never been able to have children from her womb. She said, "The ache never goes away." She went on, "But God is so good. He has been so faithful. I am thankful for my life, but it's tough when I think about it." Even now, as she lives every day with purpose and acceptance for how her story has been written, the longing for a child from her womb is enough to move her to tears because the desire to mother is rooted deep within. The ache that comes from an unfulfilled longing for a child is real and deep. God grieves with you. He also promises to bless you and give you a beautiful story.

My friend is a beautiful woman who loves Jesus and is a perfect example of what it means to mother. She has had countless opportunities to mother children through being a youth leader, and she has helped raise the three children that her husband had before they met. The thing that has hurt her most over the years has been when people say to her, "but they aren't your kids," when speaking of her husband's children. Though she never carried them in her womb, she has carried them close to her heart. Though she has never legally adopted them, she has adopted them as her own in her heart. Mothering comes in many forms, and the desire to mother is core to who we are as women – even if we never get the opportunity to grow a life within.

"Mother" the Verb

Look at Mother Theresa. Here is a woman who never carried a child in her womb, but she carried many a child in her heart. Why do you think the Catholic faith uses the word "mother" to describe or identify one who has chosen not to marry and never bare a child from her womb? It is because "Mother" is a name, but "mother" is also a verb. Mothering is something you do, and what you do reveals who you are.

Remember, we were formed to reflect God and who He is. It is weird for me to think of God as a mom. He is called Father in the Bible, but never Mother, yet since men AND women were created in His image, we know that all of the qualities that both men and women possess are encompassed in who God is. If you need further proof, look at all of creation, not just mankind.

Romans 1:20 says, *"For since the creation of the world God's invisible qualities—his eternal power and divine nature—have been clearly seen, being understood from what has been made, so that men are without excuse."*

We are told in Romans that creation is enough to tell us about who God is and what He is like. We do not need any books or testimony about God to know who He is and what He is like. His invisible qualities and divine nature can be seen in creation. Since we are created in the image of God, what do we learn from creation about motherhood?

Every animal has a mother and it is usually the mother's job to care for and protect the young. The mothers are usually the ones who feed the babies. Mothers are extremely protective and will literally lay down their lives for their young.

In addition to the nature of God that we see in animals, look at the names that have been given to the earth and the weather: Mother Earth, Mother Nature. It is no coincidence that the word "Mother" is associated with the earth and nature. People see the earth and they see it creating and sustaining the life of plants, animals and humans. We associate the attributes of creating and sustaining life with motherhood. Mother Nature is a beautiful representation of the blend of creativity and power.

Many of the Psalms paint such a good picture of the power and might of our awesome Creator. (See Psalm 104)

Psalm 19:1 says, *"The heavens declare the glory of God; the skies proclaim the work of his hands."*

In creation, we see how God captivates our heart. Have you ever gazed at a sunset and thought, "that looks familiar?" No! Of course not! Every night, He paints a different picture, and the same is true each morning. He is extremely creative and He does it to woo our hearts toward Him. Isn't that why moms cut their children's sandwiches into stars and smiley faces, or why they have special rainy day or snow day activities? They want to do fun and creative things for their children. God was the first to model this for us.

Motherhood is woven into the fabric of all of creation, including you. This is the fuel behind why we want so badly to get pregnant. We, as women, have been wired by God to mother and as we put that "wiring" into action, we reflect the nature of God that only we as "mothers" can reflect.

On the day of starting her period, a friend of mine (and sojourner on this path with us) shared with me, "As I have reflected today in my own disappointment I realize that the desire to be a mom has always been there. It is one of those things that I have always felt was a natural gift for me. Even before I became a mother myself, I mothered my brothers, the neighbors, babysat for everyone...."

In wrestling through the disappointment and trying to discern what the power behind her struggle was, this friend determined that motherhood, and all that it entails, has been a part of her for as long as she can remember.

Stasi Eldredge agrees when she says, "Not all women are mothers, but as image bearers of God, all women are uniquely called to mother. As daughters of Eve, all women are gifted to help others in our lives become more of who they truly are – to encourage, nurture, and mother them toward their true selves. In doing this, women partner with Christ in the vital mission of bringing forth life. And *all* women are life-givers."[3]

We have all been given a different God-wired assignment to mother, and we are all wired by God to bring forth life in others. Again, for those of you who are older, I hold you dear in my heart and I hope your heart hears the truth that we have just covered. You may not be a biological mother, but you are a mother. God has given you an assignment to mother along the way and even now, He has people in your life that He wants you to offer that mothering nature to. The enemy wants you to feel like you are somehow less-than because you are not a biological mother, but I beg you not to believe that lie. If you believe this lie, the enemy will succeed in preventing you from offering your God-given heart and personality to mother the people God has put in your life. You have something unique to offer the world.

When my daughter was 5, I had the opportunity to try to explain the uniqueness of being a woman to her. As most 5-year-olds are, my daughter, Alliyah, was very curious about how a baby gets *in* the mommy's belly. I think this curiosity was born, in large part, from her brother's entry into the world. In having a *brother*, she became equally curious about human anatomy. One night, I was tucking her in bed and out of the blue, she asks, "Mommy, why don't we all have penises?" I did not share with her the first thought that flew through my head, and thankfully, the Holy Spirit came to my rescue with the following response: "Honey, we have different parts on the outside, but we are also different inside. God has made us different because we have different jobs to do. Our bodies have special parts inside so that we can hold and grow the baby inside. Boys don't have that."

In the same way that we are physically made differently than men, we have a different role to play in the lives of others. We are wired uniquely by God according to the mission He has for us; and, thus, our God-given desire to mother will look different in each one of us. Our God-given mission may include many or a few children, children from our womb, or children from God's womb and given to you through the beauty and sacrifice of adoption. The problem is, we often have our own ideas of what God's mission is for us, and we may not be aware of how our plan deviates from His until we are forced to go down a road we did not want to travel.

Surrender

Before my husband and I got married, the question, "How many kids do you want?" came up often. My answer was always, "Two, maybe three," and my husband's response was always, "Three, maybe four." It's funny how when we are only speaking hypothetically, it can seem like we have some control over how our lives will turn out. Having grown up essentially an only child, I was fearful of having more than one child. I could not fathom how I would be able to give enough love and attention to more than one child.

Once we had our first child, my answer to the quantity question was, "We'll take it one at a time. We're enjoying one right now." I did not know if I would ever desire another child. I was thankful to have one. I was not prepared for the mental shift that God would work in me while I was desiring our second child. The day our second child was born, I was ready for a third. I do not know many new mothers who would say that they wanted another child on the actual birth day of one of their children. I was not ready to have a third child right away, but suddenly the question of whether or not I would want another child was a moot point. I would not only receive what God gave us, but I also WANTED another child. My "Two, maybe three," had become, "Definitely three. Maybe more."

My steering wheel had been broken in those two years that we longed for a second child. I no longer felt like I had any control over how life would turn out. I no longer felt like I needed to analyze whether or not more children would be good for us, financially wise of us, or whether or not we would have enough love and energy to give to more children. I knew that I would be able to embrace whatever God brought out way.

Something in me had shifted and it was for the better. I was losing my grip on one of the things I thought I had control of. The illusion of control that I had lived with, when contemplating how many kids I wanted, slowly drifted away as I realized that I had never really been in control in the first place. It was okay to have an opinion, but in the end, what mattered most was whether or not I was willing to embrace what God had in mind – especially if his thoughts were different than my own. My joy and peace were closely tied to whether or not I would embrace God's story for my life and not cling to my own telling of the story.

As I was forced to let go of my version of the story, I was finally able to embrace what God had given us and his timing for giving it. I saw what an incredible blessing children are. I no longer saw children as something I deserved. My thinking shifted from, *"Do I WANT more children,"* to *"Is my heart surrendered to the ways of God and to His heart?"* I found myself asking, *"Am I willing to walk the path that God has marked out for me instead of arrogantly blazing forward acting like I know the way?"*

We will only ever be free if we are surrendered. God's ways are better than our own. His ways are higher and better. Let's remember Isaiah 55:8-9:

"'For my thoughts are not your thoughts, neither are your ways my ways,' declares the Lord. 'As the heavens are higher than the earth, so are my ways higher than your ways and my thoughts than your thoughts.'"

When we stop holding on to our ways and we embrace His, we find rest for our souls. We find rest even in turmoil. As long as we refuse to surrender the issue of motherhood in our minds, we will not be free, and we will miss out on the adventure God wants to take us on. Let me be clear here. I am certainly NOT encouraging you to abandon your desire for a child. I am, however, encouraging you that motherhood does not begin when you hold your first child in your arms. It has already begun.

So what about the women who never want children? I am sure you have met women who do not have a desire to be a mom. Maybe that was you. I can understand standing on one side of a great cavern, the side labeled "not a mother" and looking across the bridge toward the other side called mother-hood and seriously wondering whether I could handle it or would be any good at it. I can also understand feeling such great purpose in your job and/or volunteering that you do not feel that motherhood would fit into the picture. To be a mom is a call to great sacrifice and unknown. Being a mom is not easy. I have never met a mom who thought being a mom was easy, and I am confident I will never meet one.

I have a good friend who, in her late thirties, was not sure if she wanted to be a mom, but she admitted to me, "All women are born with a desire to mother. I have a deep-rooted desire to mother. I just don't know if it's to my own children or if it's to minister to other people's children." This friend did not know if she wanted to be a mom, but she understood that deep in her core, she was made by God to mother. I asked her why she would choose not to have her own children. In her particular story, as I listened, I saw that every reply was laced with fear. I tried to listen carefully because the beautiful woman sitting across from me was experiencing an inner wrestle that was completely foreign to me. I so desperately wanted God to bless us with more children, while she was not sure if she would want that gift. As I listened to my friend and have listened to several others I know with her same wrestle, I have found that the majority of the time, fear is a major factor in the inner wrestle with whether or not to pursue motherhood. They fear passing on their dysfunction to their children. Oftentimes, they have had terrible mothers themselves. The struggle is real.

You and I understand the wrestle with fear. Whether you're fearful of becoming a mom or not becoming a mom, fear is fear. You do not need to fear whether or not you are good enough to be a mom. You are hard-wired to mother. You have a special and unique way of bringing LIFE to those around you. With the help of your loving, gracious Father in heaven, you will have exactly what you need to walk the path He has marked out for you. God is with you along the way. You are not alone.

Notes:

[1] Genesis 1:27-28

[2] Dialogue between Eve and the Serpent in Genesis 3:1-2.

[3] Staci Eldredge, *You Are Captivating: Celebrating a Mother's Heart* (Nashville: Nelson, 2007), 44-45.

Chapter 5

Consumed

God is a consuming fire...

"I want to want you more than I want_____."
(In this case, the blank is pregnancy.)

Hold Your Horses!

I am a horse girl. I have been riding horses since I was 10 years old and my love has not diminished as I have gotten older. In my teens, I participated in Eventing, also known as Horse Trials. At these shows, there are three different events that one must compete in and be judged. At the end, the cumulative score from the three events is tallied and the winners are announced. The middle, or second part, of the event is the cross country course. This, in my opinion, is the most thrilling part of the show because you get to run your horse through fields and woods, jumping over obstacles along the way. The hardest part of this particular event is the beginning. You have to get your horse into the starting box, which is a 16'x16' area with three sides mostly fenced in. The fourth side is open and is the official starting line for your course. Once in the starting box, you cannot, for any reason, leave the starting box across the start line until your starting time or you will be penalized. The term "hold your horses," is extremely poignant at that moment. As you wait in the starting box, the anticipation is almost overwhelming. Most people have to face their horse toward the back of the box to keep them from bolting out of the box too early. All of the muscles of the horse seem to tighten, and the moment you turn and give the horse the reins and let them run, a wild ride follows!

While the phrase, "Hold your horses," is easy for me to imagine, putting it into practice in real life is another thing altogether. Used as an idiom, the phrase means "to hold on or wait." In other words: do not rush ahead. Wait for the right time. This waiting primarily takes place in our minds, with our thoughts. If we don't point our thoughts in the correct direction, they will race off in the direction they are pointed and a penalty will inevitably result.

There are two things in this life that have caused my thoughts to run outrageously rampant in directions they probably should not go. I am not the type to stress out over a job or money or friendships. If one of these is your mental battle, then you understand the wrestle for your thoughts all too well. For me, the first thing that consumed my thoughts was boys. It is amazing how much brain power can be exhausted by thinking about, analyzing and dreaming about a particular boy one might be interested in. Actually meeting prince charming does not remove the threat of being consumed by thoughts. Human nature tells us to move on and find something new to consume our thoughts.

In my case, being consumed with a single desire was taken to a whole new level when pregnancy entered the picture. I cannot explain why pregnancy, both desiring it or thinking about it all the time if you are pregnant, can be so consuming. I just know the power it can have over a person. I am sure you understand as well. Both finding a soulmate and getting pregnant are two things we cannot force to happen no matter how hard we work to make the conditions just right. Yet, so much brain power is spent thinking about these two things in the days and years prior to the fulfillment of these two desires.

Consumed

The word "consume" is an interesting word. Did you know that the definition of the word "consume," according to dictionary.com[1] is:

1. to destroy or expend by use; use up
2. to eat or drink up; devour
3. to destroy, as by decomposition or burning
4. to spend (money, time, etc.) wastefully
5. to absorb; engross

I am going to assume that if you are reading this book, you understand what it is like to be consumed with thinking about getting pregnant. You want it so bad you are willing to do almost anything to get pregnant.

Many of us could honestly say, "I am consumed with thinking about getting pregnant." What we often fail to consider is that what we are really saying *and experiencing* is, "I am used up, devoured, destroyed, spent, or engrossed in thinking about getting pregnant." And isn't that the truth? How many of us feel run down and hopeless once we have walked the infertility road for any length of time? If we stop to think about it, we can see that allowing ourselves to be consumed with thinking about pregnancy seems a little perilous at best.

Interestingly, we find this word *consume* used to describe God in Deuteronomy 4:24:

"For the Lord your God is a consuming fire, a jealous God."

Working from the dictionary.com definition, we infer that God is a devouring, destroying, engrossing fire - which sounds horrible, at first, until we pause to consider the beauty of that statement. When we decide to give our lives over to God, God devours and destroys our sinful nature and replaces it with a pure and holy nature. He is the fire that we are thrown into to be purified like silver and gold. When silver and gold are removed from the fire, the impurities no longer exist.

God is jealous for our affection and our devotion. He does not want to share our allegiance with any other person or thing. He wants us to be completely engrossed in Him. He wants all of us. God wants to completely envelop us like the flames that envelop the wood in a fire. He wants to be our everything. Simply put, God is jealous for the energy and attention you have been giving to your desire to become pregnant.

For a long time, pregnancy was my all-consuming fire. God, unfortunately, did not fill that slot. I was giving a lot more of my time, energy and thoughts to pregnancy and my desire for a child than I was to God. And just like a fire that burns out of control, more and more of my life was being burned up, devoured and wasted by thinking about pregnancy. There is really nothing productive that comes from thinking about pregnancy or an unfulfilled desire. Allowing your thought life to park on pregnancy does not serve any beneficial purpose toward helping you to become pregnant. It also does not help you to love others better or help you to grow in your intimacy with God; it does the opposite. While being consumed with thoughts of pregnancy, I found myself growing more accustomed to thinking about myself. Without realizing it, I was sitting around waiting to get pregnant in order for my life to begin. I let my desire to get pregnant steal joy from life situations that would have normally been very enjoyable. I also missed out on investing in what is going on in the lives of those around me. What a waste.

This idea of an all-consuming fire comes to my mind every time we have a bonfire. In our family, we do not know how to have small fires. When we bought our first house, we inherited a large brush pile with it. We decided that the quickest, most effective way to take care of the eyesore would be to set the whole thing ablaze at one time. For a couple moments, I seriously feared for my life and the safety of our house as the flames licked the sky at least 40 feet high, higher than our house. The fire got hot quickly and literally consumed everything within. It was effective (all-consuming), just a little scary. When we went back inside after our fire was put out, we discovered that leaving the windows open throughout the house, with a massive fire burning just feet away, is not a good idea. The inside of our house smelled like a fire pit. The flames had consumed the brush and the smoke had consumed the inside of our home.

For me, desiring pregnancy had been like the smoke that crept in through the windows and caused everything to smell and affected the air quality for a while. There were still many moments of joy in that season, but it felt like there was always a cloud hanging overhead. The cloud was my thought life. When I was not reining in my thoughts, they were allowed to spread like smoke in a house or a wildfire on a hillside.

Unfortunately, I was not the only one who could smell the smoke. My relationships with others began to suffer as well. A relationship cannot thrive, and can barely survive, if one of the parties is consumed with themselves and unable to invest in the other party. Relationships that are one-sided rarely make it any distance because the person who is putting in all the work gets tired and burned out. As I said before, being consumed with thoughts of pregnancy only turns us inward. We spend a lot of time and energy thinking about ourselves. Our physical bodies do not help our cause. As we are acutely in tune with every ping and twinge in our body, wondering if we are feeling symptoms of being pregnant, our focus stays on ourselves. The uncertainty of whether our deep desire will be fulfilled causes us to hold tighter to the desire. Our attention is directed inward, not on the desires and needs of others.

The goal is not to put up a fake front, pretending you are not struggling. However, if you choose (it is often a conscious choice) to momentarily set your struggles aside for the sake of someone else, you safeguard yourself from falling deeply into the pit of despair. If you choose to temporarily set aside your own pain for the sake of someone else, you will find that when you return to your own issues, your struggles have come into focus a little better than when you left them. Turning your attention outward is like opening up all the windows in the house so the smoke can leave while you are gone and you can come home to a much cleaner smelling house.

I am telling you it is realistic, and more than doable, to live life victoriously, especially in your thought life. God has given you His Holy Spirit to live *inside* of you. He is called Counselor.[2] That means you have a free counselor living inside of you, offering perfect counsel every time. He will counsel you to think about what is good, right and true. He will counsel you toward loving God and loving others, if you will listen. You have a choice to listen or not. You have a choice to let your thoughts run rampant, or to rein them in. What will you choose? This is one area of your life where control is a good thing.

God, I want to want you more...

God is a consuming fire. Other things have the potential of consuming us, this we know too well. So what about this idea that God is a consuming fire? Is it possible to be consumed with Him? If so, can we become consumed with *Him* in the same way that we can be consumed about getting pregnant? How do we become consumed with God?

For me, this journey began with a simple prayer:

"God, I want to want you more than I want to get pregnant."

I am an honest person. Somehow I have been given an incredibly guilty conscience, so when I tell a lie, it eats me up inside and I cannot get comfortable until I tell the truth. Therefore, I do not lie. There have been many times I have wished this was not the case. I understand that not everyone is like this, but it is my blessing (or curse, depending on how you look at it). So for me to say, "God, I want you more than I want to get pregnant," was a lie. I was not there. I did not want God more than I wanted to get pregnant. I felt bad for that, but it was the truth. I had to be honest. God already knew, so there was no need to lie to Him.

If God truly is a jealous God, which He is, He does not want us to give our affections, our energy or our devotion to anything other than Him. He is the one who is worthy of our devotion. In Him, we will actually benefit from spending our energy. So you better believe that the tiny prayer, uttered from one of his daughters, was a very welcome request. "God, I want to want you more. I want to want you more than I want to get pregnant. I am sorry that I don't. Please help me to want you more." For the five seconds that I prayed that prayer, I was doing what I wanted to do. In those five seconds, I was wanting God more. Five seconds is a start. The more mental time and energy I put toward pursuing the Consuming Fire, the more I was slowly growing consumed with Him.

The thing about God *being* the fire is intriguing because in HIM, we are not burned. Isaiah 43:2 says, *"When you walk through the fire, you will not be burned; the flames will not set you ablaze."* We have all been burned, figuratively, by putting our trust in other things, but when we put our trust in God, it is as if we are fireproof.   Look at the story of Shadrach, Meshach, and Abednego.³ They trusted in God and refused to bow down to an idol. God was their everything. When the time came that they were thrown into a fire, they were not consumed. They did not even smell like smoke when they were removed from the fiery furnace. Or take Moses and the burning bush.⁴ The bush burned, but it was not consumed. The fire enveloped it, but it was protected. God is like that. He wants to envelop us, to fully cover and engulf us.

God IS consuming in the fact that once you have tasted his Goodness and experienced his Love, you want more. They say it only takes a spark to ignite a whole forest. The more you turn toward Him, the larger the fire grows and the more you are consumed. As you gaze at Him, He consumes all of the other things in your life that would distract you in order to leave you with a single focus: A desire for God. But a fire left unattended eventually burns out. This is why we must be intentional about keeping our mind and heart directed toward Him, lest our hearts and minds run off in the complete opposite direction - which causes all kinds of chaos and bondage.

One of the biggest threats to our thought life, and therefore to our entire well-being, is fear. Fear is consuming. Fear is like gasoline thrown on a spark of a thought. In no time, what was a tiny idea or thought has grown to a massive, difficult to contain problem.

Free not Fear

The fearful woman is the woman who wants to control. Out of our fear, we grab hold of the things we feel we can control, and we hold tight.

On the journey of desiring a child, we have learned that we cannot control when a baby is conceived, but we might feel we can control other things instead: how much and what we eat to comfort ourselves, how much we exercise, our job performance, our husbands, etc...

So what do you and I do with our control issues, specifically when it comes to pregnancy? Letting go is not as easy as it sounds. We can gain some perspective when we realize that what little control we thought we had before was really a mirage. God is the Author of Life and no other. If he does not choose to author life in you when you want it, the battle for control ensues. Ovulation Predictors, temperature taking, early response pregnancy tests, taking note of every change in your body – they **can** all be a way we try to control our situation that feels so out of control. Doing these things does not mean you are trying to take control. However, a heart check is needed because using these things can easily come from a heart that wants some control. If these are not your temptation, maybe you engross yourself in work as a distraction. We cannot *make* God author life in us now, but we can at least feel like we are doing *something* while we wait. Why do we feel like we need to be doing something? Why have we been fooled into thinking that waiting is an active verb?

"Be still and know that I am God" (Psalm 46:11).

This is a familiar verse. However, I hope you do not miss the power in the familiarity. If we know that He is God and we are not, we do not try to do His job. We trust Him to be God and we get to know Him in our stillness. You will only truly find the freedom you seek if you exchange the effort you put into controlling things for the good fight of learning to trust the Maker. Learning to bring your fears to Him so that He can deal with them is effort well spent. 1 John 4:18 says, *"Perfect love drives out fear."* We have to be still, allowing Him to love us and drive the fear far from us. You do not have to get rid of the fear, He does that. You need only acknowledge the fear and then learn how to be still in his love instead of stirred by fear. You have to choose to be still in His love. In doing so, the fear is driven away while you sit.

Let me say that again. You do not have to work hard at not being afraid. Have you ever tried to not be afraid when you were scared? They call that courage. Take heart, God asks us for only a small amount of bravery. Will you be brave enough to trust that His love for you is complete. It does not lack anything and it has the power to drive away your deepest pain and your deepest hurt.

1 John 4:18 goes on to say, *"The one who fears, is not made perfect in love."* The presence of fear is not the problem. The fact that you have fear in your life is not surprising or unexpected. What you do with your fears is the issue. You have a choice. There is always a choice. Usually the more difficult choice, the one that seems least natural, is the one worth fighting for. We are never a victim of our fears. You either choose to give way to fear, allowing it to produce bad fruit in your life, OR you choose not to fear and reap the fruit of that choice, which is peace.

When I am faced with fear, the following verse often comes to my mind. *"You are her (Sarah's) daughters if you do what is right and do not give way to fear"* (1 Peter 3:6). Do not give way to fear. The context of this verse is an encouragement for women to be godly wives. Incidentally, being a godly wife was closely linked with producing an heir and was basically a woman's sole purpose in those days. Just prior to this encouragement to not fear, it says, *"For this is how the holy women of the past who put their hope in God used to make themselves beautiful..."5* What this passage basically says is that holy women of the past made themselves beautiful by putting their hope in God, giving up control and choosing to trust and choosing not to give in to fear. Do you find it interesting that the woman chosen as our example for not giving in to fear was a woman who spent the majority of her life barren? I am sure she had more to fear than not being able to conceive, but you better believe that, in her time and culture, near the top of the list had to be the fear of not conceiving.

What makes you or I different from the women of old? We live in a different culture, but who we are deep down is still the same. We can learn a lot from them: Put our hope in God, release control, choose to trust, choose not to fear. In doing so, we will *"reap a harvest if we do not give up"* (Galatians 6:9). By not giving up, we will eat of the fruit of choosing *not* to fear. You may not have answers, but you are free. Free to enjoy life. Free to take one day at a time. Free to live.

Fear is binding, like rice or licorice. Sorry for the analogy, but constipation is no fun at all. Fear is like spiritual constipation. No one likes it, and it does not do a body good. So not only will you gain freedom if you choose not to fear, but you will gain beauty.

Fear kills beauty. Fear kills life.

Do not give way to fear. Do not give way to fear. I will say it one more time: Do not give way to fear. When you are faced with the choice to fear, do not give way to it. Is it really that simple? Yes...and no. It is not easy to choose the more difficult option because it comes less naturally. But if you are able to remove yourself from the situation, it is that simple. Which fruit do you want? Do you want the fruit in your life that comes from giving way to fear? Do you want constant uneasiness, anxiety, possible ulcers, stress, panic, worry, feeling out of control? Or do you want the fruit of the more difficult choice, choosing NOT to give way to fear: rest, trust, confidence in tomorrow, peace, even joy? I know what fruit you want, but do you want it bad enough? No one wants to be stressed or full with worry. You have what it takes to stare fear in the face and say, "No!" Luke tries to encourage us to trust when he says,

"Are not five sparrows sold for two pennies? Yet not one of them is forgotten by God. Indeed, the very hairs of your head are all numbered. Don't be afraid; you are worth more than many sparrows" (Luke 12:6-7).

You are not forgotten by God. God knows how many hairs are on your head and how many will fall out today. Do not be afraid. Your worth is so much greater than that of birds. If He is so attentive to the fate of birds, how much more so is He attentive to your fate?

Our ability to stand fear in the face comes from a solid foundation in the One who has won the victory over fear for us. Galatians 5:1 says, *"It is for freedom that Christ has set us free."* This passage goes on to say, *"Stand firm, then, and don't let yourselves be burdened again by a yoke of slavery."* Do not let yourself be a slave to your fears. Stand firm.

Jesus did not set you free so you could live your life in fear. He did not set you free from the chains of sin so you could live in bondage. He set you free so you would be free. I have heard that if a goldfish has lived in a bowl its entire life and then is set free in a larger tank, it will only swim in the amount of space they have been accustomed to.

Some of us have lived our whole lives in the fishbowl of fear, and when Jesus sets you free, you have a whole grand lake to swim and explore, but fear keeps you in a ten-inch diameter region. Throw off the chains of fear and swim. Explore. Be free!

Allow me to help you stand up to fear. Stare fear in the face and prayerfully proclaim:

"No! I refuse to be fearful that I won't get pregnant. My God is the Maker of all things. He, and no other, is the Author of Life. I am His daughter, and I have a right to ask for a child. God loves children. He has good plans for me, plans to prosper me. I choose to surrender to whatever shape those plans take in my life. He said to be fruitful and increase in number. His heart is pro-children, pro-fertility. There is no barrenness in heaven. I am fertile in the kingdom of heaven. Jesus said to pray for His will to be done on earth as it is in heav-

en; therefore, I know it is His will that I be fertile, so I pray to that end. I refuse to fear that it won't happen. I choose to trust God. I trust His heart. I trust His timing. I trust His love. I am His and He is mine."

Period. End of story. You can do it!!

Notes:

---

[1] "consume," Def. 1-5. *Dictionary.com*, http://dictionary.reference.com/browse/consume (accessed January 3, 2013).

[2] Isaiah 9:6 NIV, 1984 edition, John 14:16-17 NIV, 1984 edition.

[3] The story of Shadrach, Meshach, and Abednego is found in Daniel 3.

[4] The story of Moses and the Burning Bush is found in Exodus 3.

[5] 1 Peter 3:5 NIV, 1984 edition.

Chapter 6

Trouble Traps

"We take every thought captive and make it obedient to Christ."[1]

Freedom.

Have you ever noticed that when you are genuinely worshipping God nothing else matters? I am not talking about just singing to God. I am talking about when your heart and mind are so completely focused on God that thoughts of Him are the only thing running through your head. Something miraculous takes place, and you are able to tune your heart and mind to a single focus: God. I call this miraculous because, as women, we rarely have just ONE thing on our minds. As you worship, sometimes your mouth testifies to the peace and joy you feel within through song or prayer or testimony, but other times you are silent. You are not concerned with the weather or what you will eat later or how you are going to arrange your busy schedule to not be so stressed. You are not concerned with how you look or what is going on in a relationship. For those small moments of worship, everything else has fallen away and you are left there, alone, to commune with your Maker. These are the intimate moments. These are the raw, exposed moments. These are the moments when we are truly free.

Deep at the core of every human, and every animal for that matter, is a hunger for freedom. I have never seen an animal get caught in a trap and not immediately struggle to be free. As women, our traps are not as obvious. Often times, we do not even know what has trapped us, we just know we do not feel free. Unlike an animal trap with a door that immediately holds the animal in place, the traps that ensnare us often take a gradual approach in luring us. Over time, anything we chase after, other than God, will ultimately burn us and leave us feeling spent and used or just plain trapped.

Hebrews 12:1 encourages us to *"throw off everything that hinders and the sin that so easily entangles"* us. We all have to deal with the sin in our lives in one form or another. We all have fallen prey to the allures of this world (Romans 3:23). The words that I find most interesting in this verse in Hebrews are, "so easily." We often do not realize we are getting tangled up until we can barely move. Just like with Christmas lights, it is easy to get all tangled up, but it takes much more work and time to get untangled. In the end, the effort is worth it. So what is entangling you? Is it jealousy? Is it selfishness? Is it self-pity?

My precious second born child was practically born with a smile on his face. I know he is meant to bring joy to the world. His two dimples betray his mischievous side. He is social and loves to make people laugh. As a result, I have lost track of how many times he has landed in "reflection" (detention).

Last year, his teacher began to talk to him about "trouble traps." She explained that there are certain situations that tend to trip him up and get him into trouble more easily. He should try to recognize these things and avoid them. Wise words. Recognize your trouble traps and try to avoid them. I am sure you and I have a few trouble traps in common.

Trap #1: Anxiety

"Do not be anxious about anything, but in every situation, by prayer and petition, with thanksgiving, present your requests to God. And the peace of God, which transcends all understanding, will guard your hearts and your minds in Christ Jesus" (Philippians 4:6-7).

The second half of the fertility cycle can be the most anxiety-ridden few weeks. You wait and hope and wonder, am I pregnant or will I have to endure another month of trying? To have someone, let alone God, tell you, "Do not be anxious," can feel like the equivalent of saying, "Here, sit in this tiny raft as it heads over that waterfall down there and *do not be anxious.*" It is hard to wait and not be anxious. It is ten times harder to wait and not be anxious when the outcome is so uncertain. The key to waiting without anxiety is to take away the source of the anxiety. We are anxious because we want a certain outcome and we are not okay with the opposing outcome. We allow our joy and happiness to be a victim to our circumstances. If we get the outcome we want, we are happy – or in this case, elated. If we do not get the outcome we want, we are depressed, disappointed, frustrated, angry, or all of the above. Is it possible to *not* get the outcome we want and still be happy and joy-filled?

The writer of Psalm 116:17 writes, *"I will sacrifice a thank offering to you and call on the name of the Lord."* In order to offer thanks, the people of old had to give something up. They had to kill an animal as a prerequisite for their thankfulness to be heard and received by God because they did not have the blood of Jesus as a constant purity cloak. Thankfully we no longer need to slaughter an animal for our gratitude to be heard, but a sacrifice is still needed for our thanks to be heard. We have to kill the beast of our emotions. We have to set aside and be willing to let go of our pain in order for our thankfulness to shine through.

In Philippians 4:12, Paul tells us that he *"learned the secret of being content in any and every situation."* That means that the secret can be learned. It is truly possible to be content in *any* and *every* situation – even infertility.

The secret: Thankfulness.

We cannot feel thankful and miserable at the same time. The two emotions cannot coexist simultaneously. Therefore, we have to ask ourselves the question and choose: Do I want to be miserable or thankful? If you desire the latter, you have to set aside your emotional baggage in order to focus on thankfulness. Thankfulness is not something that comes naturally. It is a skill that can be honed and sharpened. You will never grow in this skill without practice. In order to offer thanks to God amidst your suffering, you have to sacrifice (set aside) your pain.

A week before the "worst weekend of my life," I opened my journal to lament my woes to the Lord and at the bottom of the page was 1 Peter 5:7, *"Cast your anxiety on him because He cares for you."* This is what I wrote in response to seeing that verse,

"How appropriate. I have so much anxiety today over things outside my control. I'm SO anxious to find out if I'm pregnant. I can't relax or get my mind off it. I still have probably another week before I would know. Lord, I really need your help keeping my eyes and heart on you. I know how to busy myself to stay distracted, but I want to know how to truly cast my anxiety on you."

I wrote these words, not knowing the challenge that lay ahead of me. I thought my greatest challenge would be finding out that I was not pregnant. I did not know that my greatest challenge would actually come from my external circumstances (all my closest friends getting pregnant) more than my internal ones (not being pregnant). Sometimes our circumstances seem to have arms that literally rip us out of our seat of contentment and throw us into a hurricane of emotions. It is helpful to have the practiced skill of thankfulness and to know how to cast our anxiety on God *before* we are swirling around in a hurricane.

How do I truly cast my anxiety on Him? What does that look like?

To "cast" something is to "throw, fling, throw off, throw away, direct" it.[2] You *cast* a line when we go fishing. You *cast* something aside when you are no longer giving attention to it. So to *cast* your anxiety on the Lord would be to set it aside, direct it his way, and let Him hold it. In other words, you are no longer in possession of your foul friend Anxiety if you have cast it. Because anxiety can be so consuming, when you cast it away, it leaves a hole that needs to be immediately filled; otherwise, anxiety will come whipping back like a boomerang to make its permanent home. Again, thankfulness is the solution. I recommend replacing the time and space that anxiety used to fill with thankfulness. First, you choose to hand your anxiety to God and then you immediately put energy toward being thankful. As you invest in being thankful, there will be no room for anxiety. You will grow thankful for the "here and now" and less concerned about a future that you cannot control. This is how you take away the power of anxiety. The negative outcome of the monthly cycle does not carry the same punch when it runs into the heart that is filled solid with thankfulness.

So throw off this anxiety that has kept you in bondage for too long. God is the only one who has the right to tell you not to be anxious. He knows that anxiety does nothing to help you – it only harms. Anxiety takes your heart and mind and focus off of the One who can truly comfort you during whatever you have to endure.

I have heard that stress and anxiety cause many physical ailments such as: ulcers, indigestion, heartburn, and cold sores. Anxiety can even cause your body to produce symptoms that make you think you are having a heart attack. I know several people who have thought they were having a heart attack only to find that they were having a panic attack – an anxiety attack. Thankfulness, on the other hand, causes joy to well up in you and brings peace, contentment, love, and a new perspective. If you choose thankfulness, you will undoubtedly find yourself taking note of the small joys you had neglected to notice before.

Trap #2: There must be something wrong with me.

When we saw our fertility specialist, Dr. Dodds jokingly gave my husband "the blue ribbon award" for the highest sperm count they had seen in six months. His sperm were bountiful and healthy. Clearly the problem was not with him.

No one likes to think there is something wrong with them. We battle these thoughts our whole lives. That guy we have a crush on doesn't return the affections... "*What is wrong with me? I must not be pretty enough.*" We don't get the job or promotion we seek... "*What is wrong with me? Why didn't they pick me?*" Our friend suddenly seems more interested in cultivating another relationship... "*What is wrong with me, why don't they like me?*" Now we are faced with the very thing we were created to do, bear life, and we can't... "*There is something wrong with me.*"

Whether or not you have been diagnosed with an explanation for your fertility issues, the nagging thought remains: "*What is wrong with me? There is something wrong with me.*" I say this with the greatest amount of love I can express on these pages: What good do you think it will produce to worry about, or dwell upon, what is or might be wrong with you? What good will come from that? Anything?

On the flip side, what if you choose to think about the goodness of God? What if you choose to think about how much God loves children and that He shares your desire that you bear life? What if you choose to think about how no physical ailment is too challenging for the Healer to take care of? What good would come from choosing that second line of thinking? Could any bad come from it?

Here we have a choice again. What fruit do you want? Do you want more anxiety or do you want to put your fate in trustworthy hands and watch and see what He does?

We will look at some of the common physical ailments that can contribute to infertility in Chapter 7, but sometimes the answer to why we are struggling is not clear-cut. We go to doctors to find answers and sometimes we find them. Other times, the solution is not as easy to find. What we do know is that any and ALL physical concerns when it comes to fertility were dealt with on the cross. The Bible says in Matthew 8:17, when Jesus died on the cross, *"He took up our infirmities and bore our diseases."*

Sickness and disease are a result of sin. Before sin entered the scene, sickness and disease and death did not exist. I think we can all agree that we do not *yet* live in the originally designed world. Jesus lived in our broken reality, too. Therefore, He hung on the cross, a sinless man, in order to buy our freedom from sin and brokenness. He hung there to bring restoration to the whole world. He hung on that tree, accomplishing a restoration that would be **fully** realized at a later date. Jesus restored things to the way they were before sin for those who would accept what He did for them. For those who accept this reality, the restoration begins inside the person and will one day be the reality for the whole earth. Am I losing you here? Stick with me. Romans 10:9 says,

"If you declare with your mouth, "Jesus is Lord," and believe in your heart that God raised him from the dead, you will be ***saved****"* (Emphasis mine).

I majored in Spanish in College, so I know that when you study a foreign language, it is not always possible to translate a word perfectly into another language. In translation, some of the meaning from the original language can be lost if you try to translate word for word. The same is true as we look at the Word of God because the languages in which it was originally written were Hebrew (Old Testament) and Greek (New Testament). So as I studied this verse in Romans, I went to my Hebrew-Greek Key Word Study Bible and learned that the Greek word that we translate into "saved" is the word "sōzō" (pronounced like sode- zo).[3] The definition that the KeyWord Study Bible gives for the word "sōzō" is: To save, deliver, rescue, to heal, make whole, preserve from danger, loss or destruction.[4]

The word God gave us as a promise that we will be "saved" means so much more than we can fathom. The word sōzō is used over thirty times in the Gospels (Jesus' ministry). In fourteen instances where sōzō is used the saving refers to being delivered from disease or demon possession. In twenty in-stances, the saving refers to the rescue of physical life from some impending peril or instant death.⁵ To be "saved," as we see in Romans 10:9, clearly refers to a physical healing, not just being rescued from hell.

Here is where I get really excited: This same word, sōzō, that is used in Romans 10:9 is the same word that is used in Matthew 9:20-22 & Mark 5:24-34 to describe the healing of the woman who was bleeding for twelve years.⁶ Before I retell her story, let me ask you this: If she was bleeding for twelve years, do you think she could have children? I have bold-printed the words that were translated from the word sōzō.

Here is her story from Mark 5:24-34:

*"A large crowd followed and pressed around him. And a woman was there who had been subject to bleeding for twelve years. She had suffered a great deal under the care of many doctors and had spent all she had, yet instead of getting better she grew worse. When she heard about Jesus, she came up behind him in the crowd and touched his cloak, because she thought, "If I just touch his clothes, I will be **healed**." Immediately her bleeding stopped and she felt in her body that she was freed from her suffering.*

At once Jesus realized that power had gone out from him. He turned around in the crowd and asked, "Who touched my clothes?"

"You see the people crowding against you," his disciples answered, "and yet you can ask, 'Who touched me?'"

But Jesus kept looking around to see who had done it. Then the woman, know-ing what had happened to her, came and fell at his feet and, trembling with fear, told him the whole truth. He said to her, "Daughter, your faith has **healed** *you. Go in peace and be freed from your suffering"* (emphasis added).

I could just weep over how beautiful this story is. Can you see yourself in that woman's shoes? I do not know the full extent of your suffering. You do not have to have suffered for twelve years to understand her pain. Maybe you have suffered longer. She had spent all she had. She pursued doctors, but no one could help her. She knew her only hope was in this man, Jesus. And did you hear His words to her, His words to you? *"Go in peace and be freed from your suffering."*

Aahhhh. Can you imagine your pain and suffering being released in an instant? That is what Jesus is offering you right now - even before your fertility journey is resolved. *"If you confess with your mouth, 'Jesus is Lord,' and believe in your heart that God raised him from the dead, you will be* **SAVED**" (Romans 10:9, emphasis added).

Jesus broke the curse of sin and death.[7] We are no longer cursed. You are no longer cursed with infertility if you confess Jesus is Lord. We have the authority and power of God living in us, through the Holy Spirit, to proclaim healing in our physical bodies. When Jesus died on the cross, He restored creation to its original state, the state that existed before sin. We are waiting to see this reality fully realized. This restored state is already accomplished completely in heaven. Jesus told us to pray that God's kingdom would come and His will would be done on earth as it IS in heaven.[8] In the heavenly realm, your body and my body work completely as they should.

If you have dealt with your doubts about God's heart, you can rest in the fact that it is NOT God's will, nor His heart's desire, that you be infertile. There is no support in the Bible saying that God is pro-infertility. Jesus broke any power that the enemy and his tools of sickness and disease have over you. Thus, you need only to stand firm, choosing to believe: You are whole, without defect, washed clean, made new because of what Jesus did on the cross. When you stand firm, it is not too much of a stretch for you to wait in expectation for your reality from the heavenly realm to be brought to earth. Again, Jesus told us to pray, "Your Kingdom come and your will be done, on earth as it IS in heaven" (Matthew 6:10, emphasis added).

Allow me to summarize what you have just read. The doctors may have found a diagnosis for why it has been difficult for you to conceive. That knowledge can be very helpful as you pray for your body to be restored with the healing that Jesus bought on the cross. You are not, however, doomed to the diagnosis. Healing can happen. If a doctor is the tool that God chooses to use to heal you, that is wonderful. Our amazing second born is a testimony to God using doctors to bring healing. Just remember that it is still God healing you, even if He uses medicine to do it. Whatever the method, the truth remains: Jesus bought your healing. Will you receive it, as you stand in faith, believing it is yours to possess? Do not let your experiences do the talking. Let God do the talking through his Word and through His Spirit. We stand firm in faith until what we believe becomes the reality we experience. This is what it means to believe and not doubt.

Or maybe your infertility is a mystery...to you. God sees and knows why you are dealing with infertility, and He offers healing to you, no strings attached. He will not hold back healing until you have learned some lesson. He already bought your healing on the cross. It is already accomplished.

Trap #3: There must be something spiritually or emotionally wrong with me that God needs to fix first.

If God is not changing your situation now, it is easy to assume that there is something God needs to teach you first. This assumption is not necessarily based on truth. Remember Job? He was afflicted. He suffered but did not do anything wrong to deserve it. When Jesus healed people, He never told them to get clean first. He always addressed their sin AFTER He healed them (Read the Gospels). From this we can conclude that it is not the nature of our King to hold out on healing us to try to teach us a lesson. On this side of heaven, there will always be opportunities to dwell on something we perceive as "wrong with us." God does not want us to focus on what we think is wrong with us, He wants us to focus on what is right with us. Remember: Jesus made you whole again when he died on the cross.

"Therefore, if anyone is in Christ, he is a new creation; the old has gone, the new has come" (2 Corinthians 5:17).

He has made all things new. In Jesus, we have been made new. You have been made new. New things are free from faults, defects, wear and tear. They are new and fresh. The old is gone. You are new and fresh. You do not need to be "fixed" before He will bless you with a child. You are already perfect. You are whole.

It is strange to live in the both/and. Jesus has already made us whole, and at the same time, His Spirit is at work to help us be whole. Both realities are fully true. Jesus's death made us whole from a heavenly, spiritual perspective. In the physical world we live in, we still struggle with sin and brokenness, and we are in the process of being made whole.

His Spirit is always at work, moving us toward becoming like Him. It is in our best interest to embrace the good work He is doing, regardless of where we are on the journey. Here is a soul-searching question: If you try to "be better" because you want something in return, are you truly embracing change? Your outward actions do not always mean that you are different on the inside. A true transformation happens when the only reward being sought for embracing growth is the reward of knowing God and being more like Him.

I have not always understood the goodness of embracing God's transformation for the pure joy of becoming more like Him. Here is a continuation of what I wrote in my journal after that weekend in May 2008 that I call *the worst weekend of my life*:

"I can't take any more, Lord. Please show me some other way what you want me to learn. How much longer do I have to walk this road? Father, I can't help

but think I'm not special to you – you hear me, but I need something more. I need you... I know that my hope needs to be in you. I'm sorry that I'm not satisfied in you. I'm sorry that I roll my eyes at the verse at the bottom of this page (Jeremiah 29:11). Father, I don't feel prosperous. I do feel harmed...oh, I'm so tired. Please help me 'trade my sorrows.'"

I had bought into the notion that I needed to learn something before God would stop my suffering. I wanted to hurry up and figure out what that "something" was so I could get pregnant. My motivation to embrace growth from the Holy Spirit was a bit self-seeking. What God wanted for me was to recognize that He is always at work, and He wanted me to embrace what He was doing in me without strings attached. If you can embrace the growth opportunities He presents, with a heart that is surrendered, not wanting something in return, then you are in a great place.

God does not operate by our rules. He does not demand that we be perfect before He is willing to heal. He does not even ask us to be good first. Look at the ministry of Jesus for example. He healed and then said, "Go and leave your life of sin" (John 8:11). He addressed their behavior *after* He healed them. Many times, He first spoke to the person, "Your sins are forgiven," when they came to Him for physical healing.[9] The spiritual and the physical are intimately connected and God cares about both, but one is not a prequel to the other. What God wants to see is a heart that is humble before Him, waiting to receive His goodness – not because we deserve it but because of His great mercy.

Trap #4: There are so many teen pregnancies and other people getting pregnant who don't want to be pregnant, and I really want to get pregnant. Why can't I?

At the heart of this question lie two struggles: Jealousy and doubting God's heart and His ways.

God's possible quick answer to our question is this: *"As the heavens are higher than the earth, so are my ways higher than your ways and my thoughts than your thoughts"* (Isaiah 55:9).

The month before I conceived our second child, I was presented with a familiar opportunity to examine my heart. I found out that my sister-in-law was pregnant with her second child. This was person #30 on the list I had made that proved everyone was getting pregnant except for me. When I found out she was pregnant, I wish my only emotion or thought at the moment was joy and excitement on her behalf. Unfortunately, that was not the case. I'm sure you can guess what I was feeling. I was jealous. I wanted to be pregnant, too. Since our oldest children are so close in age, I found myself suddenly desiring pregnancy much more than I had the moment before I received the news. I had been in such a good place with my heart genuinely settled on these things: *I trust God's timing and His ways. I am thankful for the perfect spacing of my children. I am thankful for the child I have. I am thankful for the many other wonderful things in my life.* In an instant, I went from cruising along smoothly on the train of contentment to rolling in the dirt of anxiety, wondering how I was thrown from the train.

It only takes one small thing to throw us off course. Let's revisit the story that takes place in Genesis 3:1-7. God had shown Adam and Eve all the things they had access to and the ONE thing they could not have. Satan enters the picture and says, "Let's talk about that one thing you can't have." Satan turned Adam and Eve's eyes away from the abundance that they had toward the one thing they couldn't have. Can you guess how Satan works this strategy in our lives today?

Jealousy is a deceitful pair of glasses. When we are jealous, we are staring at the thing we cannot have and wanting it for ourselves. As Adam and Eve stared at the forbidden tree, the longing grew until they could not contain it. They reached out, grabbed, and ate the fruit. And we continue to eat the "fruit" of that decision today. The fact that you and I are dealing with infertility is a "fruit" of that decision.

So the question remains: What fruit is being born in your life? Have you been staring at the thing you deeply desire so much that all other things have faded away? Has the desire for a child become so all-consuming that other things in your life have begun to suffer? If, upon honest assessment, you find some rotting, decaying fruit that you have picked up along your journey, now is the time to discard it. The antidote? Taking back control of your mind and choosing thankfulness. 1 Thessalonians 5:18 commands us to:

"Give thanks in all circumstances
for this is God's will for you in Christ Jesus."

I really struggled with this verse because I just could not say, "God, thank you that I am not pregnant." I could not do it. I have not met anyone who, when desiring pregnancy, could genuinely say that. Yet people would say, "God commands us to be thankful." Eye roll. Then I realized that I had been reading this verse incorrectly. It says, be thankful *in* all circumstances not be thankful *for* all circumstances. This makes a huge difference! I did not have to be thankful that I was not pregnant, but God was telling me to choose thankfulness while going through that circumstance of not being pregnant. Big difference! The first is impossible, the second is difficult, but doable.

Once you are yanked from contentment, it takes work to get snuggled back into your spot on the contentment train. First you must seize your thoughts, no longer allowing them to run wild. Once you have reined in your thoughts, you have control over where you will direct them. God suggests we direct our thoughts toward thankfulness. We can be like Adam and Eve and become consumed by what we don't have OR we can make a better choice and choose to be thankful for what we do have.

"I have learned the secret of being content in any and every situation, whether well fed or hungry, whether living in plenty or in want"

(Philippians 4:12).

Will you accept the challenge to learn the secret that Paul learned? I know you want it. I want it, too. I want a contentment that cannot be shaken, no matter what trouble trap, no matter what hurricane occurs. The anchor, the secret, is thankfulness.

Notes:

---

[1] 2 Corinthians 10:5

[2] "cast," Def. 1-3. *Dictionary.com*, http://dictionary.reference.com/browse/cast?s=1 (accessed January 3, 2013).

[3] "sōzō," Hebrew-Greek Key Word Study Bible NIV. Spiros Zodhiates, Th.D., Executive Editor Hebrew-Greek Key Word Study Bibles, Warren Baker, Managing Editor, NIV Edition et al. (Chattanooga, TN: AMG Publishers, 1996), p.1324 & 2117, entry #5392.

[4] sōzō," Hebrew-Greek Key Word Study Bible NIV. Spiros Zodhiates, Th.D., Executive Editor Hebrew-Greek Key Word Study Bibles, Warren Baker, Managing Editor, NIV Edition et al. (Chattanooga, TN: AMG Publishers, 1996), p.1676, entry #5392.

[5] sōzō," Hebrew-Greek Key Word Study Bible NIV. Spiros Zodhiates, Th.D., Executive Editor Hebrew-Greek Key Word Study Bibles, Warren Baker, Managing Editor, NIV Edition et al. (Chattanooga, TN: AMG Publishers, 1996), p.1676, entry #5392.

[6] sōzō," Hebrew-Greek Key Word Study Bible NIV. Spiros Zodhiates, Th.D., Executive Editor Hebrew-Greek Key Word Study Bibles, Warren Baker, Managing Editor, NIV Edition et al. (Chattanooga, TN: AMG Publishers, 1996), p. 1676 (Romans 10:9), page 1136 (Matthew 9:20-22), page 1324 (Mark 5:24-34).

[7] Romans 10:4, Galatians 3:10-13, Romans 8:1-2

[8] Matthew 6:10, emphasis added.

[9] Matthew 9:2-8, Mark 2:5, Luke 5:20, Luke 7:47

Chapter 7

The Medical Facts of Life

*"Cast your cares on the Lord and he will sustain you;
he will never let the righteous be shaken."* [1]

The Battle

Surprise! Your period is here. Period? What!? How many of us have been completely caught off guard with the starting of our period? Some would have to think back to teenage years to remember a time when the period came unexpectedly. For others of us, it is the busyness of life or a mis-calculation that has allowed us to be surprised. At some point, most of us have been surprised by that crimson flow that momentarily stops us in our tracks. If your mind is *not* consumed with thoughts of pregnancy, the stop is only momentary. You take care of business and you are back on your way. If you're trying to conceive a child and the unwanted visitor arrives, the train stops for longer.

The blockades on our tracks that often derail us are called hormones. Hormones complicate matters in general, but when you are dealing with infertility, they really wreak havoc. Since I didn't struggle with extreme hormone fluctuations until later in life, I always thought PMS was a myth or an excuse for women to be mean or irritable once a month. I was wrong. According to the Mayo Clinic, as many as 75% of women experience some level of premenstrual syndrome (PMS), with depression near the top of the list.[2] That's 3 out of every 4 women.

Depression caused by PMS is not necessarily circumstantial; it is hormonal. The feeling of depression that I am speaking of is not caused by outside influences; it is caused by a hormone that is influencing from the inside out. Balancing our hormones and chemical make-up can be a complicated feat even if that was the only factor. For the *trying to conceive* (TTC), matters are exacerbated by the fact that while our hormones are urging, "Be depressed!" our circumstances are also giving us reason to be depressed. It's a double whammy. You are legitimately disappointed and sad from not being pregnant AND your hormones are working against you. Fighting one of these factors alone is no small feat, but pair them together, and the battle seems too great.

The battle IS fierce. The feeling of depression is real, but we do not have to be a victim to the feelings we have. My mother-in-law says, "You can't trust your feelings." It used to really bother me when she said this because up until the point of battling hormone-assisted depression, I had not experienced a time when my feelings had seriously led me astray. The majority of the time, when I felt something, it was a somewhat accurate indication of an ongoing reality. As I experienced my time of TTC, I began to see the wisdom of what she was saying.

You have a choice.

You can choose to respond according to what you know to be true and good and right, or you can give in to your flesh and be led accordingly. Here is the choice I suggest you make: Choose to fight depression with truth instead of letting your thoughts go crazy. You can choose to focus your mind on what is true: *I know my hormones are making me feel down. I do not want to feel down, so I can refuse to listen to my hormones.* This means that when you feel depressed, you have a powerful tool to wield. Name your depression for what it is. Hormonal.

I do not want to make this sound easy or simplify a very real issue. I know that some of you who are reading this struggle with the chemicals and hormones in your body that create a legitimate clinical depression. This depression is its own entity, aside from the depression that comes with a monthly cycle or with circumstances that are challenging. Sometimes it takes medicine to help level things out. Remember, God heals miraculously and He heals using medicine. As we continue forward in talking about depression, we are addressing what we can do to fight the mental battle. If you need additional help from a medical professional in fighting the physical realities and causes of depression, there is no shame in that. Ultimately, depression is not from the Lord. When our bodies are warring against us, causing depression, our bodies are not operating the way God intended them to, so it is in our best interests to fight for what God DOES intend for us: Wholeness, peace, and joy.

Recognizing that your hormones are most likely affecting your ability to feel happy can be the key to setting you free from experiencing such *extreme* lows on your journey. As long as you face infertility, you will still have to deal with the disappointment and sadness, but it is helpful to recognize that you are battling in the physical as well as the spiritual. For most people, there are plenty of circumstances in life to bring us down. If you are not in tune with the natural cycle of your body, you might mistakenly assume the depression you face simply has to do with one of the things life has thrown at you. The danger of focusing on your circumstances and how they are making you feel is that you give depression a greater opportunity to sink its ugly talons into your soul.

Tuning in to Your Body

Recognizing you have a choice in where you park your thoughts, is part of the solution to living depression-free (or at least not overcome by depression) in a season of waiting. The other part of the solution is to be in tune with the natural cycle of your body. When you are in tune with what is going on in your body, you are better able to understand and fight for your emotions to be kept in check, and you are more likely to discern hormonal influences. If someone says something to me and I recognize a fiery response welling up, it is helpful to know if I am at a time in the month where hormones might be contributing to my passion.

What I am suggesting is not easy. Feelings can be powerful and cause us to act in ways that we know are not beneficial. A friend of mine explained her experience to me this way: "I found myself being extremely b**chy this week. As I was yelling at my husband, I was thinking, 'What am I doing?'" She recognized that her response was not solely the result of the interaction she had had with her husband. Hormones were affecting things - negatively affecting things. When our hormones are working properly, everything in our body is at peace and our hormones are level. When our hormones are out of whack... well, you know what comes. Chaos. That chaos can transfer into any area of our life. The enemy of our soul is just waiting for an opportunity to do some damage to the important relationships in our lives. Do not let yourself be duped.

If you respond to people based on how you are feeling all the time, you run the risk of damaging your relationships – especially when your feelings are hormonal. Having a *feeling* does not give you a right to act on it. How much more devastating are your words or actions when your response is driven by hormones and not from something the other person has done or said? That person is blind-sided. Similarly, I have found that if I recognize when hormones may have played a part in my interaction with someone, it is easier to humbly admit my wrongdoing to the other person. You feel less like you need to stubbornly hold on to your position in the argument if you recognize that some of your passion was rooted in hormones and not entirely in what you think about the matter. Hormones are not an excuse for saying or doing anything you want.

Natural Family Planning

Let's look at how you can be in tune with what is going on in your body. Natural Family Planning (NFP) is a good tool to help you do just that. NFP teaches you how to recognize the natural signs that God has given you to determine where you are in the fertility cycle. Many people use NFP as their method of contraception and others use it to try to get pregnant. In this chapter, I want to give you an overview of some of the nuggets of gold you can glean from NFP. I do not claim to be an expert on NFP, and this is not a "How To" guide to using NFP. I recommend signing up for a class or buying a book on NFP if you are interested in learning how to use NFP either for contraception or conception.

In the last chapter, we addressed our control issues. Please keep *freedom* on your mind as we navigate this chapter. Fight to use NFP to bring you to a place of greater awe in the Maker of all things, who has caused everything to work together so intricately and mysteriously. I warn you against learning about NFP as a means to try to take more control. Remember, we experience greater freedom and we are more at peace if we are surrendered to the timing and good plan of the Creator.

How NFP works:

It uses Basal Body Temperature (BBT) as one of the primary ways of tracking your cycle throughout the month. BBT is the temperature of your body when you have been at rest for an extended period of time and there are no external factors affecting your body temperature. You have the best opportunity to record your BBT if you take your temperature in the morning BEFORE you get out of bed. It is recommended to us a digital thermometer that registers a temperature to the hundredth decimal point. NFP also recommends that you take your temperature at the same time every morning to get a more accurate tracking. As you chart your temperatures each day, you will notice a pattern. The pattern looks slightly different for each woman, but if everything is working smoothly, there will be similarities amongst all women. Generally, your temperature will slowly, continually drop from the day you start your period until it reaches a low just before you ovulate. On the day you ovulate, your temperature will noticeably increase and remain in an elevated range until the end of your cycle or will remain elevated if you get pregnant. If your temperature drops after remaining elevated in the second half of your cycle, that is a good sign that Aunt Flo is about to visit[3].

What about seeking medical assistance?

I had been charting my cycles with NFP and gaining a greater understanding for how my body works for several months before my husband and I sought medical assistance in conceiving our second child. Before we met with Dr. Dodds, our fertility specialist, I had heard that he was a Christian. In our first meeting, I asked him point blank, "Are you a Christian?" It was helpful for me to know where he stood so I could know where he was coming from as he was treating us and advising us. I was also curious about how another

Christian handles fertility matters. I am not typically this blunt with a person I do not know, but I was relieved to find that my question did not shock or rattle him. He easily responded that he was a Christian and was happy to share more about his beliefs, especially as it related to his job. He explained that it can be difficult to be in a field with so few believers as colleagues. I had never really given it much thought, but it surprised me to hear that very few of the fertility doctors in the nation are believers. I guess I figured that if they desire to participate in God's miracle of creating life, many would know Him. Dr. Dodds suggested that maybe it was because the field can open the door to many controversial discussions. Some believe that if we seek medical assistance for conceiving a child then we are trying to "play God." I can understand this line of thinking. I have wrestled with this very idea myself.

Before my husband and I decided to pursue medical assistance, we talked with a few people who had sought medical help to conceive a child. Our close friends, Jim and Angie, had seen Dr. Dodds and explained to us that they were very thankful they did had sought medical assistance. Jim shared with us his belief that God wants us to have children, so he would not balk at doing whatever he could (morally) to make that happen. This was the little nudge I needed to make the decision to contact Dr. Dodds. Up until that point, I had been in a constant wrestle. I pondered the questions: *If we seek medical help, will God bless it? Are we just trying to make things happen on our own time without trusting Him?* In my questioning, I forgot to consider the fact that the Spirit of the Living God lives in me and He promises to guide me (2 Corinthians 1:22, John 15:26).

I realized that the way I was thinking about fertility issues versus other medical conditions did not line up. I would not hesitate to take Tylenol if I have a bad headache. Is it really so different? God did not create me with a headache. Having a headache is not His good and perfect design. He created me to be whole, healthy, and without pain. Likewise, God did not create us to be infertile. He commanded Adam and Eve to "be fruitful and increase in number." Why wouldn't I pursue medicine to solve infertility issues if I was willing to take Tylenol to solve a headache?

I had to remind myself of this again when we were on round two of battling infertility. Even after learning all that God taught me the first time around, I still found myself not wanting to pursue the medicine route again to conceive our third child. I realized that I was believing the lie that if God helped us get pregnant without medical help, then that was somehow better. Let me say that again. That line of thinking was a lie. Whether God uses medicine or the miraculous, it is still Him giving the healing. One is not better or worse than the other.

I just wanted God to do it. If I was honest, I did not want to have to go through the treatments again. This was the passive approach. It does not take much investment or relationship (with God) to just wait for something to happen. On the other hand, if we are actively pursuing the heart of God as it relates to how many children He wants us to have, then we build intimacy with our Maker. Being active instead of passive is not about trying to take control, it is about being active in the pursuit of God and the things that please Him. It is about continually surrendering our hearts and desires to Him and letting Him lead us. I knew he wanted us to have more children. I just did not want to have to go through medicine again. When I realized that the reason I did not want to pursue medicine was because I thought that it was a second-rate healing, I was convicted.

Being healed through medicine and being healed through the miraculous are both equal healings from God. In both sides of the coin of healing, we can get side-tracked and miss what is important. Those who witness the miraculous can get caught up in the gifts that God gives more than being caught up in WHO He is. Those who are healed through medicine can turn and thank medicine and forget the power behind the medicine. I do not know why God chooses to heal through the miraculous sometimes and through the medicine others, but the common denominator is the heart of our Maker who wants all things to be restored to their original design. He is the Healer behind the miraculous AND medicine. I have experienced both and can testify to the fact that neither is greater than the other. Both healing are gifts from God.

Using medicine to restore fertility...

If you are like me, you like to know how things work, but might be clueless about how it all works together. When considering the pursuit of medical assistance, I wanted to know exactly what I was getting myself into. I tend to ask a lot of questions. Thankfully, we had a wonderful doctor, Dr. Dodds, who was patient and willing to share any information I needed to feel informed and at peace with the decisions we were making.

I asked Dr. Dodds if he would be willing to answer a few questions for this chapter, and he gladly obliged. In case you are like me and you find it helpful to understand how everything works together, the following are the questions that I asked Dr. Dodds and his responses.[4]

What made you decide to be an endocrinologist?

"I became a Reproductive Endocrinologist because, as a medical student, I was excited by this area as the most cutting edge area of medicine at the time. Louise Brown, the first "test tube baby" was born in 1979 when I entered medical school. In addition, I had the experience of meeting a great mentor, Dr. Moon Kim, who encouraged me to enter this field. I feel God led me to this area of medicine. I see being a fertility specialist as my call to serve others with the gifts God has given me."

What is the usual progression you take a couple through if they are seeking medical treatment for fertility issues? What are the basic initial tests you run and what are the questions you ask in the beginning?

"**Key Questions** include:

1) How long has the couple tried to conceive? The longer the time period generally means a more significant issue.

2) What is the age of the female? As age increases, especially past 35, fertility decreases rapidly.

3) Are there any prior surgeries in either the male or female?

4) Have there been any prior pregnancy successes?

5) Is there any family history of early menopause, infertility, or endometriosis?

6) Does the female have significant pelvic pain issues?"

"Infertility evaluation requires a careful history and complete physical exam. 80% of infertility issues involve problems in one of three areas: 1) Male factor 2) Tubal factor problems 3) Ovulatory issues."

"The Key Tests that we typically run are:

1) Evaluation of ovulation via basal body temperature (BBT) charting, mid-luteal serum progesterone testing and mid-cycle ultrasound to evaluate follicle (egg) and uterine lining development. If a patient presents a simple ovulatory dysfunction, we often skip hysterosalpingogram and semen analysis until after correcting ovulation and seeing if the couple conceives with ovulatory treatment alone over a four month period.

2) Semen analysis with strict morphology

3) Hysterosalpingogram to evaluate tubal factor.

(this includes having a dye injected through your cervix that travels into your uterus and through your fallopian tubes. A technician then watches on a screen to be sure that there are no blockages in your tubes.)"

What are the most common causes of infertility that you have seen?

"The most common causes of infertility are as follows:

1) Male factor (40%-50% of cases). The most common causes are genetic, prior injury, toxins and medical illness.

2) Tubal factor (25%-30%). Primarily due to pelvic infection, endometriosis, and prior surgery.

3) Ovulatory Dysfunction (15%-25%). Primary causes of ovulatory dysfunction are: polycystic ovarian disorder, fibroid disorder, diabetes, obesity, and stress.

4) Endometriosis (5%-15%). Causes are unknown."

What can you tell us about Natural Family Planning and fertility?

"Natural Family Planning utilizes the menstrual cycle information to optimize pregnancy success. It is important to note that cycle to cycle variability **is natural**. One does not need to time intercourse to the day of ovulation to become pregnant. Pregnancy chance does increase by ensuring adequate sexual activity is occurring. To optimize pregnancy success, sexual activity should occur 4 to 5 times during the mid-cycle 10 day period (i.e. cycle day 10 to 20 in a 28 day cycle). Another way to use natural family planning to aid in conceiving a child is to establish when ovulation is occurring using basal body temperature or urine LH surge detecting kits or doing cervical mucus checks and timing intercourse 4 to 5 times starting five days before to five days after approximate ovulation. 80-90% of couples should conceive within 1 year if the female is less than 35 years of age. If pregnancy has not occurred in one year the success is 40-70% at one year. Patients older than 35 that have not conceived after six months, should seek expert fertility care. Early intervention is important because of more limited time to achieve the pregnancy goal."

What would you say are the main hormones that affect our reproductive cycle? Could you give a brief description of what each one does and how each affects us if they are out of balance?

"<u>FSH (Follicle Stimulating Hormone) and LH (Leutenizing hormone</u>) are key pituitary hormones that stimulate oocyte (egg) development. Low FSH and LH leads to poor oocyte development and infertility.

<u>Thyroid</u> – Low thyroid leads to tiredness, poor sleep, headaches, loss of hair, dry skin, poor oocyte development, infertility, and increased miscarriage rate.

<u>Estradiol</u> – Estradiol is the hormone produced as eggs and the uterine lining are developing. Estradiol is both a product of good egg development and a stimulant for good egg development. Low estradiol leads to menopausal symptoms such as hot flashes, low energy, poor sleep, infertility, and bone mineral loss.

<u>Progesterone</u> – Progesterone is the pro-gestational (pregnancy) hormone. Progesterone stimulates specific changes in the uterine lining to allow embryo implantation. Low progesterone leads to increased miscarriage rate, infertility, and possibly preterm labor.

<u>Prolactin</u> – Prolactin is primarily significant when excess amounts are present. If excess amounts are present, this can lead to suppression of FSH and LH that then leads to poor egg development."

Knowledge is Helpful

There are so many hormones in our body that are intricately connected and serve different functions. I only asked Dr. Dodds to describe the ones that specifically relate to fertility, but there are so many more hormones in our body that work together to make everything in our bodies function properly.

A woman's fertility cycle is such a mystery and every woman's cycle is different. I'm writing this as I'm on my period. This month, my cycle began on day 22. Only 22 days since the last period. Goodness! I have a friend who regularly has 45-60 days between her cycles AND she merely thinks about being pregnant and she is. That does not seem fair, does it? This friend knows her body very well and can clearly determine when she is fertile and when she is not. She has been practicing NFP for many years. In the end, it does not matter how your body compares to another, what is important is that you know your own body.

I understand that if you have never been all that in tune with your body and the natural signs that God has given to help you understand your fertility cycle you may have quite the learning curve ahead of you. If you are a little overwhelmed with the information I just shared with you, you are not alone. I have a friend who, when at the beginning of seeking medical assistance to conceive, had the doctor tell her she had 4 eggs. She had no idea what that meant. Feeling somewhat like a hen, she asked, "How many eggs should I have?"

Maybe you are content to be like my friend and not fully understand how things work. That is just fine. Ultimately, our peace during this season is not found in fully understanding what is or is not going on; it is about trusting the Maker of all things. Our Maker has made our bodies so complex that it can be mind-boggling at times. Doctors and scientists have spent hundreds of years studying, experimenting, and learning through trial and error to get us to the place we are at today in our understanding of the human body and medicine. There is still so much we do not know or understand.

I am not a doctor, and I am content to leave trying to fully understand the complexity of the body to them. However, I am extremely thankful for the doctors and nurses who have the heart and desire to help others be well. They get to take part in God's healing. What a cool job. God says to the surgeon, "Today we are going to heal this person so they can walk again and you are going to make it happen. I am going to use your hands. I will guide you." Or maybe He says to the nurse, "Do you see this grumpy old man? Look past his gruff exterior. Inside he is hurting. Love him for me, will you?" I am sure God has used you to bring healing to others with an encouraging word or just a smile, and when He does there is nothing greater on this side of heaven. The fact that the Maker of the Universe allows us to take part in His work is a grand privilege.

Sometimes God does not use "miracles" (unexplained healing) to bring healing. He wants to give others the joy and satisfaction of having helped another human being. God is a great delegator. He could do all the work him-self, but, because of His great love for us, He invites us to participate with Him. This is where medicine fits into the grand design. Do you see medicine as God healing? When you take a Tylenol or Motrin, do you thank God for that medicine and for healing your aches and pains or do you thank the medi-cine? If I am honest, for most of my life, I did not consider God in that equa-tion. I did not thank God nor did I thank the medicine. If I had a headache, I would go to the medicine cabinet and take some pain killer and go back to business. I did not ask God to heal my headache, and I did not thank God for the healing when it went away.

When I was begging God for a miracle with my son so he would not have to have surgery at 11 months old, someone shared these words with me, "You go to God first, asking for the healing. If you do not see the healing, then you go to medicine. Either way, it is God bringing the healing. You just give yourself the opportunity to witness a miracle if you go to God first." Until then, I had honestly not considered that medicine was a huge way that God heals. Also, I realized that so often my hope and trust for healing had been in medicine, not in the One who is greater than medicine. He is the One who made man and gave man the brain and resources to come up with modern day medicine. Where is your trust?

Concluding thoughts

If you are the one walking this special path called infertility, I am guessing it has been a while since you have been caught off guard with the starting of your period. You have probably been fully aware of the timeframe you could be expecting this unwelcome guest. As you have sat and hoped and prayed that your period would not come, you have probably analyzed every air bubble in your stomach, every cramp, every tingle in your breast. *Are my breasts getting sore? Is the egg implanting? Do I feel nauseous? I think I feel tired...* We want to be pregnant so bad, I wonder if we make our bodies manifest the symptoms of being pregnant. It is helpful in these moments to know and understand your body and the God-given signs that we have to help us understand our fertility cycle. G.I. Joe says, "knowing is half the battle." The other half of the battle is the fight. Thankfully your victory has already been won for you.

The fact is, when Jesus died on the cross, He broke the curse of sin and death. That means that even our hormones are no longer a "curse" to us to bring death (by way of depression, for example). We can exercise authority over our hormones and not be a "victim" to them. The battle over our hormones is truly won in claiming the victory we already have because of what Jesus did AND in taking control of our minds. Having the knowledge to understand the physiological changes in your body can help you travel this road toward fertility. The other half of the battle takes place in your mind. The expected and unexpected challenges that come from desiring something that you have minimal control of can be the most fertile ground for mastering the skills needed to fight for your thoughts.

Notes:

[1] Psalm 55:22

[2] Mayo Clinic Staff, "Premenstrual syndrome (PMS): Overview," *Mayo Clinic, https://www.mayoclinic.org/diseases-conditions/premenstrual-syndrome/symptoms-causes/syc-20376780* (accessed March 30, 2020).

[3] John F. Kippley and Sheila K. Kippley, *The Art of Natural Family* Planning, 4th ed., (Cincinnati, OH: The Couple to Couple League International, Inc., 1996). Information stated about Natural Family Planning is a summary of information learned in this NFP book.

[4] Doctor William G. Dodds, founder of The Fertility Center, located in Grand Rapids, MI, "has received recognition through a peer nomination process as one of the best doctors in his specialty, Reproductive Endocrinology. This achievement places him in the top 1% of Reproductive Endocrinologists across the nation. Dr. Dodds was also one of the top 5 Spectrum Health physicians included in the list of U.S. News Top Doctors." This information is according to http://www.fertilitycentermi.com/nationallyranked/ (accessed January 3, 2013).

Chapter 8

LIVE in the moment

"Delight yourself in the Lord and he will give you the desire of your heart." [1]

"Rejoice in the Lord always. I will say it again: Rejoice!" [2]

Blood stains are not easy to get out of underwear. Can I get an Amen? The last thing anyone in our situation wants to do is scrub their underwear as a result of finding out this is not the month that will usher in a new season. If you don't get a stain out fully, it is there to remind you of your unwelcome surprise every time you wear those panties. Some choose to completely throw that pair of panties in the trash rather than deal with the stain. I have done that. Unfortunately, we cannot do that with our hearts. When our heart is scarred from the circumstances of life, we can not toss it in the trash. The reminders of our non-pregnant or childless reality come in different forms, but they have one thing in common. They threaten to rip us from being fully present in the moment, causing us to dwell on the past or the future. There is no *easy* solution for these unwelcome reminders. But God does offer a solution if we are brave enough to consider it. Check out what God commands us to do in Philippians 4:4:

The pregnant friend calls. We are told: *Rejoice in the Lord always.*

The due date of a miscarried child comes and goes. Again we are told: *Rejoice in the Lord always.*

Another friend tells you she is pregnant. *Rejoice in the Lord always.*

Your co-worker was pregnant at the same time as you, but you have miscarried and have to daily watch her grow as you would have. *Rejoice in the Lord always.*

A family member gets pregnant. *Rejoice in the Lord always.*

The eager grandparents ask again, "When are we going to have some (more) grand babies?" *Rejoice in the Lord always.*

There goes another pregnant belly in the grocery store. *Rejoice in the Lord always.*

The period starts. *Rejoice in the Lord always.*

Are you annoyed with me, yet? Did you think of throwing this book at the wall? If I were you, I would be thinking things like, *"How can she tell me to rejoice? This is tough. Do you know the definition of the word rejoice? Easier said than done. This is unrealistic. Thanks for pointing out another thing I'm not doing right..."*

In chapter 6, we talked about taking our thoughts captive and making them obedient to Christ. If I got you riled up, feel free to take a moment to rein in those thoughts if you need to. I genuinely mean no harm. I apologize if the scenarios above hit too close to home. The above scenarios are our reality, aren't they? There are bountiful opportunities for our pain to surface. I urge you to continue on this journey with me. If the emotion has surfaced, you are in a good place. A pastor friend of mine says, "You can't heal what you can't feel."[3] A wound needs to be exposed to the air to heal properly. If you are feeling exposed right now, know that your Maker covers you with His love and wants to put salve on those wounds. If we allow our pain to be exposed, we can be healed. God's Word is like Neosporin for our wounds. As God does His healing work in us, something new grows over the wound: An unshakeable joy. Joy that emerges through pain is somehow stronger than any other joy we experience.

Joy

It appears as though we are taking the battle in our mind a step further. It is a very difficult undertaking to keep your thoughts under control, but it is another thing altogether to think about having joy in the midst of difficult circumstances. Is that what I am suggesting? Am I really suggesting you fight for more than just having control of your thoughts? Is joy in tough situations really attainable?

I think so. Paul, the apostle, thinks so, too. He is kind of bossy and pretty much commands us to rejoice.

But rejoicing is not something you can force. You cannot force joy. If we could, there would be a whole lot more happy people in this world and a lot less drugs. If we cannot force ourselves to be joyful, then what is Paul getting at here? The word "rejoice," means, "to be glad; take delight; make joyful; gladden."[4] If we plug that definition in to Philippians 4:4, we get:

"Be glad, take delight, be joyful and gladdened in the Lord, always."

You may not be able to feel joy in your *circumstances*. That is not what God is calling you to. He is not telling you to put on a smile and pretend like you enjoy this bumpy road. He is not telling you to try to find the silver lining of joy in the circumstance. He is, however, asking you to remain loyal to rejoicing *in Him*. He is asking you to remember the goodness of God, regardless of what is going on in the world around you.

There is an unshakeable joy found in the Lord. Look at the incredibly heroic stories we hear of people being put in jail and tortured to within inches of their lives and yet, they worship the King. Their hope remains unwavering in Him. It is ridiculous to suggest that they found a way to have joy in their circumstance. Nothing about their circumstance could produce joy. That is why God tells us of this joy that transcends circumstances. Rejoicing is less about a feeling and more about a change in perspective that leads to an unshakable joy – shifting our focus toward Christ and not on our circumstances.

How do we get the unshakeable joy?

In the Lord, there is joy, a gladdening of the heart, that is waiting for you. *In the Lord*. What does that mean? This concept is kind of obscure. I remember hearing on a number of occasions, "If you are happy, tell your face." If we are truly happy, it will show on our face. I have also heard countless messages about the joy that Christians are supposed to have, and for many years, these messages brought condemnation for me. I did not feel like I lived with the kind of joy that I was supposed to have as a believer. I wanted joy. I did not understand why I failed to possess "the joy of the Lord."

It was on this journey through infertility and engaging in the battle for my thoughts that I began to see why I may have been lacking the elusive joy people spoke of. Until facing infertility, I had always been able to find joy in my circumstances. I could plan something to do that I could look forward to. I could buy something new that would temporarily make me happy. I liked God. I wanted to love Him, but I honestly did not know how to love Him. It took the testing of my love for Him to reveal what love, if any, I genuinely had for Him. It took living through circumstances that were less than desirable in order to move me toward loving God for who He is, not for what He does for me.

Let me say that differently: Infertility was the fire. My faith was thrown into the fire in order to test whether there was any genuine love for God. The product that came through the fire was a lot smaller than what went in to the fire, but it was pure and solid. The fluff that surrounded my faith was burned away and I was left to look at what my devotion to God really looked like. When our faith is tested, we get the opportunity to see where our hearts really stand. I was able to see if there was any real love for God in my heart instead of a love that was based on how good my life had been up until that point. Genuine love is not based on what someone does. Genuine love originates in you and is freely given without any strings attached. For a long time, I parked on the following verse:

"Delight yourselves in the Lord, and he will give you the desires of your heart" (Psalm 37:4).

I struggled with this verse. I felt like I loved God. I did a lot of things for Him, so why wasn't He giving me the desire of my heart? I was reading this verse as a cause and effect kind of thing. If you want a child (the desire of your heart), then delight in God. So all I needed to do, was work at delighting in God, then He would give me a baby.

The problem with this line of thinking is that is keeps the thing you desire on the forefront of your mind. Your number one priority is still the thing you want, not God. The object consuming your mind is still, just that, an object (the desire for a child).

In his book, <u>Crazy Love</u>, Francis Chan asks probing, beneficial questions:

"Do you believe that God is the greatest thing you can experience in the whole world? Do you believe that the Good News is not merely the forgiveness of your sins, the guarantee that you won't go to hell, or the promise of life in heaven?"

"The best things in life are gifts from the One who steadfastly loves us. But an important question to ask ourselves is this: Are we in love with God or just His stuff?"[5]

To rejoice, or find joy in the Lord, is to look to Him, not the gift, for that gladdening of the heart. We find the *joy of the Lord* when we choose to focus on and give energy to thinking about who God is and all that He has done for us. We find true joy by choosing to believe in His goodness, a goodness that transcends our circumstances.

In our face-paced, egocentric culture, there are a lot of distractions. It is very easy to think about, dwell upon, and give energy to things other than God. Yet, God is always there. Amidst all our busyness, He beckons us. He is trying to draw us away from our distractions so we can find the thing that will finally satisfy: Him. God will not demand our attention or our worship even though He is so deserving of all our affection.

Again, Francis Chan counsels, "In our world, where hundreds of things distract us from God, we have to intentionally and consistently remind ourselves of Him."[6]

It seems ridiculous to think that we would need to remind ourselves of God when his creation cries out and testifies about Him. But how many of us spend more time in man-made things (buildings) than God-made things (nature)? Even 100 years ago, people spent the majority of their time outdoors. There were still distractions, but not the enormity of distractions that we currently face on a daily basis. In our present age, it takes intentionality to be mindful of God; it will not just happen. So let's take a moment to look at the life of Jesus and how He victoriously navigated this earth.

The JOY of Jesus

Since Jesus is the perfect representation for what it means to be human and do "human" well, how did He do it? How did He remain joyful in all circumstances? He cried out to the Father. He recognized that true joy is found *in* God, and He knew He could not do life successfully and joyfully without the Father's help. In crying out to the Father, His focus and ambitions were pointed in the right direction. His focus was on the Kingdom of God, and the result was joy and peace.

Here are the words of Jesus, *"Do not store up for yourselves treasures on earth, where moth and rust destroy, and where thieves break in and steal. But store up for yourselves treasures in heaven where moth and rust do not destroy, and where thieves do not break in and steal. For where your treasure is, there your heart will be also"* (Matthew 6:19-21).

Jesus is trying to help us see that EVERYTHING of this world will eventually pass away. It can never fulfill us and could be taken away at a moment's notice . Only the kingdom of God and all that the kingdom entails can deeply satisfy. The more we prioritize talking with God, learning about Him, and putting into practice what we learn, the greater our joy and satisfaction.

In the garden of Gethsemane, we get to see Jesus putting this very principle into practice.

Luke 22:39-44 says, *"Jesus went out as usual to the Mount of Olives, and his disciples followed him. On reaching the place, he said to them, 'Pray that you will not fall into temptation.' He withdrew about a stone's throw beyond them, knelt down and prayed, "Father, if you are willing, take this cup from me; yet not my will, but yours be done." An angel from heaven appeared to him and strengthened him. And being in anguish, he prayed more earnestly, and his sweat was like drops of blood falling to the ground."*

On the verge of the greatest challenge He would ever face as a human, Jesus fell at the figurative feet of the Father. He knew that He could not walk the road He was being asked to walk without the help of his Father in Heaven. Falling at the Father's feet did not necessarily mean that His circumstances would change, it just meant that He would be strengthened *in* His circumstances.

Hebrews 12:2 says that Jesus endured the cross *"for the joy set before him."* It was the promise of future joy that gave Jesus the strength to endure the cross.

"Let us fix our eyes on Jesus, the author and perfecter of our faith, who for the joy set before him endured the cross, scorning its shame, and sat down at the right hand of the throne of God. Consider him who endured such opposition from sinful men, so that you will not grow weary and lose heart" (Hebrews 12:2-3).

I recently read an article on Facebook about an alleged conversation that took place in a philosophy class between a student (Einstein) and his atheist professor. After I saw this article, I googled it to see if it was a real story. Most people think it is unlikely that this conversation actually took place in real life, but even as a story, it paints a good picture for how to make sense of the good and evil in our world and how God fits into all of it.

The scenario goes something like this: The professor asks questions like, "Do you believe in God? Is God all-powerful? Is God good? Who created evil?" (Haven't we all wrestled with these questions?) The professor attempts to prove that, according to science, God cannot exist. The student replies that it takes faith to believe in God's existence. The student uses the examples of cold, darkness and death to make his point, arguing that these things in and of themselves do not exist as a measurable entity. According to science, in order for something to be proven that it exists, it must be measurable. Cold cannot be measured, but heat can. Heat is energy and therefore can be measured. We cannot measure how cold something is, we can only measure how much heat is present or absent. Cold is the term we use to describe the absence of heat. Stay with me here. Likewise, darkness cannot be measured, but light can. We cannot measure how dark something is, but we can measure how much light is present. Darkness is the absence of light. Finally, death is not something in and of itself, it is the absence of life. In conclusion, evil is not a "thing" that was created, it is the mere absence of good – the absence of God. God did not create evil, its existence is tied to God's existence. It is not a created thing, it is simply the absence of God.

Many people say they cannot believe in the existence of God because they see all the evil in the world and they have no other explanation for why evil exists other than to conclude that God created evil. That is clearly not the case. God created Satan, but then Satan chose to walk away from God and into darkness – thus, God banished Satan from His presence. Satan is the product of choosing to be absent from God.

What does this have to do with joy?

Everything. You see, Jesus endured the greatest anguish any human can experience (an undeserved, agonizing, slow death), yet He did not fall prey to despair. There was an unshakable joy that awaited Him on the other side of the cross. While Jesus was in the Garden of Gethsemane, we are told that He wept and was in such great anguish that He actually sweat blood. I always thought He possessed such deep anguish because He did not want to have to go through the physical torment, but now I realize that He was not agonizing over what His body would endure. He was agonizing over the fact that He would be absent from God for three days before rising to be with the Father again. Three whole days!

Many of us have fallen prey to depression and despair as we have travelled this infertility road. Sometimes it feels like there is no way to escape the huge pit of depression. If you struggled with depression before facing infertility, then there is a good chance infertility has not helped your battle against depression.

Let me ask you this: Is it possible to feel the presence of God and feel depressed at the same time? Give that some serious thought. I am not suggesting that fighting depression is simple or easy, but I do want to point out that if depression is winning in your life, there's also a good chance that you feel quite distant from the Lord. When you feel near to Him, depression does not have the hold it once had. When we can see depression for what it is - the perceived absence of God - the solution is: Increase God, starve the depression. Simple, yet extremely difficult and complicated to live out. If you turn up the "heat" in the God department, you will feel His warmth. Depression is a cold, lonely place. Draw near to God and He will draw near to you, and there will be no room for depression. Every step you take toward God is a step away from depression. Depression can be characterized by darkness and hopelessness – in other words, the absence of light and the absence of hope.

All of the "immeasurables" have one thing in common, they are the absence of something good. And since God is GOOD, they characterize the absence of God. God is light and He is good. Dark and Light cannot co-exist. Hot and Cold cannot co-exist. One will overtake the other – and guess which wins?

Light and Heat!!! Light and heat have to decrease or leave in order for darkness and cold to be present. Depression and joy play by the same rules.

It sounds simple on paper, but applying this truth to our lives takes real spiritual muscle. It may take additional assistance as well. Depression takes place in our minds, which means our minds are where the battle needs to begin, but as we discussed earlier, depression is often caused by (or at least assisted by) chemical imbalances in the body. There is no shame in seeking medical assistance to help overcome the large hurdle of depression.

When depression is present, there is an absence of God from at least part of our thinking. If we increase God in our thinking, we decrease depression. Consequently, depression is also the absence of joy and if we want joy in our lives (who doesn't?), the answer, again, is to insert more God.

When we are depressed, we do not necessarily want God. We lack the motivation or desire to go to God in times of trouble if the majority of our relationship with God has been characterized by our feelings. If we are close with God only when life is good, our faith is extremely weak, at best, and will not serve us well when we are despairing. The fire of infertility has probably already revealed to you what substance of your faith remains. If you don't like what you see, don't feel bad. Knowledge is power. It is better to have an honest assessment of your faith than an over-inflated one. You have an opportunity right now to exercise your faith muscles in order to grow stronger. When we are depressed, we do not *feel* good about anything, really. This is why it has to be a *choice* to draw near to God rather than waiting around for it to feel natural. Draw near to Him and He will draw near to you.

Joy is something you can possess. It is something you can cling to and hold on to and claim as yours. The secret is found it clinging to and holding on to God. Jesus clung to God for the joy that would come through the pain. There is joy on the other side of your pain, too.

Thankful

I recently read another wonderful book that I wish I would have found when I was going through infertility the first time around. In Ann Voskamp's book, One Thousand Gifts[7], Ann describes her own struggle to fight for joy, a joy that is not necessarily rooted in circumstances. She encourages readers that thankfulness has to be learned, even practiced. This book has helped me with this concept of finding joy in the Lord.

Ann had a friend challenge her to write a list of 1000 things that she loved. God turned her quest to name 1000 things into a list of thankfulness. In acknowledging that you love something, you can take it a step further to thank God for it. In doing so, you begin to form a list of things you are thankful for. By naming the things, writing them in a list, instead of just thinking about them in a passing thought, you are able to truly receive each beloved item, big or small, as a gift from God.

When I was half-way to 1000 and also in the midst of desiring our third child, I added:

522. Carnival atmosphere.

523. Treasures found at a garage sale.

524. The confidence to talk with people I don't know very well.

525. Outdoor worship services

526. Lakes

527. Watching children play tag

534. Strength to not give in to my flesh (self-pity)

535. Finding out Keisha is pregnant!

On the day I wrote these, I was fighting a mental battle where I wanted to give in to self-pity. I was on my period. As I fought, I was feeling as though I had the upper hand on my thoughts - in large part because of a choice to be thankful. When I found out Keisha was pregnant, I realized that all my fighting had paid off. I smile at realizing that, even though I was in the thick of desiring another child for myself, I could genuinely say that I was extremely thankful that my friend was pregnant. I was thankful, not because it benefited me, but because I knew how deeply my friend has desired to get pregnant. I could share in her joy.

Each situation that comes your way is an opportunity to respond. How you respond will determine the fall-out that you have to live with. If a difficult situation is before you, you can respond by turning inward and only reflecting on how the situation has affected you, OR you can turn your face upward and talk to the One who sees the big picture. He is the only one qualified to counsel you about how you should respond to the circumstances of life. He is always there to remind you that, like Transformers®, there is "more than meets the eye." There is always a lot more going on than what you can see. If you focus only on how you have been affected or how you feel in the situation, you will never see the big picture. Similarly, two people will struggle to be in a good relationship with one another if, when a conflict arises, one of them *only* sees the conflict through the lens of how *they* have been affected. In order to resolve conflict in a healthy manner, both parties need to be able to hear each other's point of view. Both parties need to understand and be understood. In your relationship with God, He is already doing his part. Are you?

Genuine Love

It is in your best interest to fight to stay present and respond wisely in whatever moment you find yourself. Your relationship with God is on the line and so are your relationships with other people. Jesus commanded us to first love God, then love others the way we love ourselves. The acronym of the word J.O.Y. reminds us how to prioritize: **J**esus, **O**thers, **Y**ourself. If your priorities are kept in this order, you will not be lacking joy.

Love is all you need. The greatest thing is love. If you don't have love, you have nothing. These are common phrases regarding love. Every day that passes, I grow more convinced that love is the answer to all of life's problems. I also realize more and more how difficult it is to genuinely love well.

This past week, I was faced with a situation where I knew I needed to offer love, but love was the last thing I was feeling. I had a person in my life take a comment I had made and twist it so far from the truth of what was said that she found a way she could be offended by it – something I could not believe was even possible from the comment I made. She proceeded to spread the wrong information to others as well as being unwilling to talk it out with me so I could set the record straight. She was so caught up in her self-created reality that she was not able to see what was really going on. She was not even able to see any fault she had in the situation. It blew my mind. I knew that it would be good and right to offer her love. Jesus said to love our enemies and pray for them. Romans 12 encourages us to NOT repay evil for evil but to overcome evil with good. I remember saying to God, *"But she doesn't deserve my love,"* and I remember His gentle response, *"You don't deserve my love either."*

Pause...Oh. Uh-huh. I get it.

God was helping me to see something. If it is this difficult for me to love someone who has been so unkind to me, how much more difficult must it be for God to love me. There are so many more offenses that I have committed against Him than anyone has ever done to me, yet He loves freely. By choosing to love her when she did not deserve it (in my mind), I was given the opportunity to grow in my depth of understanding of God's love for me. I had a choice. I could love this person, or I could treat her the way her actions told me she deserved to be treated. In my eyes, she did not deserve love, but neither do we, yet Jesus modeled pure love. If I treated her the way I would have wanted to, it would have been easier and more satisfying in the moment, but the long-term effects would have been harder to live with.

You have your own daily opportunities to decide how you will treat people and respond to them. If you are too caught up in your emotions and the things going on in your life, you will not be able to love others well. You will not have J.O.Y. you will have Y.O.J. or Y.J.O. Either one of the last two sound pretty silly. You are going through an incredibly difficult time in your life, but that does not excuse you from the greatest command Jesus ever gave: Love God and love others.

No Fear

We already talked about fear, but it is worth revisiting here, especially as it pertains to love. Fear is the opposite of love. If love trusts, hopes, perseveres (1 Cor. 13:7), fear does the opposite. Fear causes us to doubt (lose trust), look inward, and stop dead in our tracks. Nothing threatens to rip us from the present or cause us to look to our circumstances more than fear.

What is it you currently fear most? Not having this coveted child from your womb?

I love the quote, "Courage is not the absence of fear, it is the judgment that something else is more important than what you fear."

To have courage to truly live – even in a roller coaster season that can include much sorrow – you must judge that something else is more important than your fear of not conceiving. You must conclude that fellowship with God and the joy He gives are more important than getting what you want.

1 Peter 3:6 references Sarah (the first woman in the Bible to struggle with infertility) and says, *"You are her daughters if you do what is right and do not give way to fear."*

Do not give way to fear. We all fear that it won't happen. We fear that our deepest desires will not be satisfied, and so we cling to them even harder. Freedom can only be found with an open hand, not a clenched fist. Opening your hands and releasing your desires into the hands of the One who can be trusted with the results, is the only way to true freedom.

You have to fight. You have to choose. When you fight well and choose wisely, the outcome is always good.

Stay in the Present

In addition to standing firm and not giving way to fear, you have another battle in your mind: staying fully present in the moment. I have spent the second half of countless months analyzing the tiniest changes in my body, wondering if I'm pregnant, meanwhile allowing my mind to rocket into the future. There's the calculating of when the due date would be, what season it would be, who else would be due at that time. If it is your second child, you might even start thinking about the schedules of who would be able to watch your oldest while you are at the hospital. You think about the holidays and how pregnant you would be for each momentous occasion in the next 9 months... On and on go the thoughts. All of these thoughts are spent giving energy to the future – and to a future that is not certain, not guaranteed.

Three times in the book of love called Song of Solomon, God's word says, *"Do not arouse or awaken love until it so desires."*[8] Many a teenager has been counseled about sexual purity using these verses because we all know that if you open the box, you want to see everything that is inside. Eventually, you have emptied the contents of the box and you are left unsatisfied because the contents of the box were meant to be enjoyed in the context of marriage.

Pregnancy and desiring love are so similar when it comes to our thoughts. Be honest here. Are you guilty of calculating the due date of a child you do not know if you have conceived yet? Have you allowed yourself to daydream about how pregnant you will be at various life events coming up and what sorts of things will be happening around your "due date?" All of this "second life" has been dreamed up in your mind before you know if you will be pregnant this month. As you think and dream, your heart follows. As a result, your heart takes an even greater blow when you receive the undesired news that you will have to wait at least another month. *"Do not arouse or awaken love until it so desires."* Do not allow the affections of your heart to be ignited and excited about being pregnant until they have the fuel (an actual pregnancy) and freedom to burn strongly and brightly. Do not spend so much time in your future that you miss out on the present.

Your energy is better spent here, in the present.

This is a good rule of thumb that goes beyond the fertility journey. Our culture is always looking toward what's next. When my daughter was 5, she would wake up each morning and ask, "What are we going to do today?"

When I would give her an answer she would then ask, "What after that?" She and I would continue in this line of questioning until we reached an answer that she was excited about. From such an early age, we want to know what's next. We struggle to live in the moment.

Some battles are worth fighting. Consider the outcome if you are able to live fully present in the moment you are in: You will be able to soak up each moment. Your relationships will be carefully tended instead of being neglected by busyness and distance. You will be at peace, with the ability to enjoy and notice what God has for you NOW, instead of wondering what is next.

God has you right where you are, doing what you are doing, for a greater purpose than to just get through it. There are co-workers who need love and encouragement, neighbors who need a hand, family members who need attention, relationships that need strengthening... the list goes on. God puts people in your path each day. He gives you countless opportunities to partner with Him in bringing light and love to a dark and broken world. Acts 17:26-27 says,

"From one man he made every nation of men, that they should inhabit the whole earth; and he determined the times set for them and the exact places where they should live. God did this so that men would seek him and perhaps reach out for him and find him, though he is not far from each one of us."

He has determined the times set for you. He has determined the exact place that you live. God did this so that you would seek Him and perhaps reach out for Him and find Him, though He is not far from you.

Don't miss out on the intimacy to be had with God, as you partner with Him in bringing his Kingdom to earth. Look up and out as opposed to down and in as you walk through your day and you will be surprised how many God-appointed opportunities you have been given. What an adventure!!!

Be intentional about finding out about what is going on with other people. Think of questions you can ask people who are dear to you when you are not with them. Keep track of what is going on in their life and follow up with it. Practice love. Practice thinking about others. Practice makes perfect. You would be amazed at how relieved you feel when you take some of your focus off yourself and focus on others instead.

An easy burden

Jesus said, *"My yoke is easy and my burden is light"* (Matt. 11:30). He never meant for us to be loaded down with all kinds of baggage. He promises to walk alongside us, offering what we need when we need it. The burden to love people well does not need to be mustered from our own strength.

He meant for us to be "yoked" to Him. In Biblical times, a yoke was a set of interpretations about the Scriptures. Each Rabbi had their own set of interpretations, and if you wanted to follow a Rabbi (to model your life after them), you had to receive their yoke and accept it as your own. So when Jesus says that His yoke is easy, He is saying that His set of interpretations of the Word of God are easy. You can follow them. Just follow Him.

Also in ancient times, and in some societies still today, oxen were the power for the plow. They did not have large green tractors to do the work. The oxen provided the energy needed for the fields to be tilled. They worked in teams, yoked together. That means that Jesus offers to be a team with you. He is strong enough to carry the load if you get tired. Just don't forget He is right next to you.

Jesus easily spelled out what God really wants from us: *To love God and love people.*[9] I appreciate the simplicity. All of the deep mystery and interpretation of the Scriptures rests on those two commands. Jesus's yoke is not complicated, and He is the power behind that yoke. He is the one who helps us to love Him and others. The Bible also says in 1 John 4:19, *"We love because he first loved us."* The overflow of His love for us allows us to love others. The more we sit and soak up and receive His love, the more we are able to live fully in the moment, no matter what circumstances are swirling around us.

Notes :

[1] Psalm 37:4

[2] Philippians 4:4

[3] Rob Link, Pastor of The River, Kalamazoo, MI

[4] "rejoice," Def. 1-2. *Dictionary.com*, https://www.dictionary.com/browse/rejoice?s=t (accessed March 30, 2020).

[5] Francis Chan, *Crazy Love: Overwhelmed by a relentless God (Colorado Springs, CO: David C. Cook, 2008), 62.*

[6] Francis Chan, *Crazy Love: Overwhelmed by a relentless God (Colorado Springs, CO: David C. Cook, 2008), 29.*

[7] Ann Voskamp, *One Thousand Gifts: A dare to live fully right where you are* (Grand Rapids, MI: Zondervan, 2010).

[8] Song of Songs 2:7, 3:5, & 8:4.

[9] Matthew 22:36-40

Chapter 9

Joy Comes in the Mourning

"Rejoice with those who rejoice; mourn with those who mourn."[1]

"Blessed are those who mourn, for they will be comforted."[2]

Disclaimer: I want to tread carefully as we walk this next piece together. The grief that accompanies loss can be crushing and is not something to quickly gloss over. This book is meant to be a companion as you walk the path of infertility. Loss and grief are an inevitable part of that journey. Entire books have been written to help navigate loss and grief. We will not be able to exhaustively cover how to work through your grief, but hopefully God's truth illuminated on the next pages will help shine light into your darkness and help bring you hope and peace.

Jesus knew loneliness.

For all eternity, Jesus had known perfect fellowship, being one with the Father and the Spirit. Yet, when He hung on that cross, He was completely alone. The Spirit was temporarily restricted. For that moment in history, the Father allowed Jesus to be taken from His presence. Jesus had become sin, taking our place in punishment (2 Cor. 5:21). The Father, being perfect in nature, could not co-exist with anything imperfect; otherwise, He would be tainted. In the same way that pure water and dirty water cannot mix without the pure water becoming impure, God could not enjoy fellowship with His beloved creation (mankind) while His creation was still covered in the grime of sin. The cataclysmic solution came when Jesus willingly accepted blame for every horrific choice (sin) made by every human.

There was mourning in the heavenly realm. The enemy was rejoicing. The Son of God, the Lamb of God was slain. Thankfully, that was not the end of the story. God knew that the mourning was temporary. God knew that the enemy's rejoicing would quickly end. But in that instant, the weight of the world's sins pressed down on the shoulders of a perfect man. Jesus knew that this had to take place, yet He still cried out, "Father, Father, why have you forsaken me?" Have you asked a similar question?

Jesus understands.

Sometimes the weight of the circumstances we are in is too great, that no manner of understanding for "why?" can satisfy. Jesus knew why He had to hang on the cross, yet as He hung there, in spiritual (and physical) agony, the question still came: "Why?"

I have a dear friend who is now in her early 50s. She got married later in life, not fully expecting that marriage would happen for her. She is an elementary teacher, a perfect fit because she loves children. She has wanted to be a mom for quite some time. She called me in August of 2011 to tell me that she was officially pregnant after a second round of in-vitro. She and her husband had been trying to conceive since they got married (over 4 years). Something supernatural had to be keeping me from jumping out of my skin because I was so excited for her. I wanted to leap through the phone and hug her. I'm sure I looked like a freak show as I danced around the room because it was the only way to deal with the excitement within. She emailed me three weeks later to let me know that she was in the process of miscarrying.

What do you do with that? Such immense joy and hope for the future turned to mourning in an instant.

Why?

I am sorry if this hits close to home. Stick with me.

Flash forward to the summer of 2013. This same dear friend, 45 at the time, was pregnant again and eagerly looking forward to meeting her daughter. She was 34 weeks pregnant when she came to my house so our horses could get their feet trimmed. She mentioned that she hadn't felt her daughter kick that morning. I tried not to be too alarmed, but I suggested she call her doctor. Her doctor told her to go straight to the hospital. As I drove my friend the 20 minutes to the hospital, we were both in a war of emotions hoping that in just a few moments all our fears would be laid to rest and she would see that beautiful little girl on the ultrasound screen.

My friend's husband met us there and went back to the room with her. As I waited in the waiting room, I prayed desperately for everything to be okay. Time slowly ticked by. I finally asked the receptionist if there was a way I could get in touch with my friends. A few moments later, I was led back to her room and when I opened the door, I knew. Her daughter was already in heaven. The three of us bitterly wept together.

Why?

Maybe you understand these scenarios too well. When I read the email about my friend's miscarriage and when I entered that hospital room, I cried. I still get tears in my eyes as I remember those moments. I felt pain with her. My heart was broken for all that she had to go through and for the challenges she faced. I did not feel the depth of anguish she was feeling, but I was tapped in. I know my friend uttered her share of questions to God. *"My God, why have you forsaken me? Why have you forgotten about me? Do you not see how much pain this has caused? Were you powerless to stop it?"*

When we are sad, we are drawn to these types of questions. Somehow we seem to forget all that we have learned, and we once again question God's goodness and His power. We cannot make sense of why we are experiencing what we are experiencing, so we look for someone we can toss our emotional baggage onto because the weight is too much for us to carry. If we blame God, it feels like we have something we can do with the surge of emotion welling within us. We know that if we do nothing, we will burst, so we lash out – often at God. We need to release the emotion. Although not deserving, the God of the universe is the best equipped to handle our lashing out.

Unfortunately, our family and friends can become the victims of our lashing out, as well. We say things like, "You can't possibly understand." We invalidate the help they are offering just because they have never walked in our shoes. Maybe we lash out by criticizing something in their life. In some twisted way, we don't want their help because their lives are too perfect. We think, *they haven't experienced real pain like this.* In our pain, we push people away.

Like a confused, distressed swimmer, we lash out at the one trying to save us. Lifeguards are trained to offer a flotation device to a distressed swimmer because, if they get too close, the drowning victim may try to use the lifeguard as a flotation device, thus putting both of their lives in danger. Our family and friends are people that God uses to bring comfort, but they cannot compare with the comfort He alone can give. If our loved ones are trained lifeguards, they know to offer us the ultimate flotation device: the Life-saver, a.k.a. Jesus. In order to victoriously navigate through our pain, we have to find a way to cling to the Life-saver rather than trying to use our friends as flotation devices. Our friends just don't have the strength to hold us up for very long without the help of Jesus. If we hold on tight and wrap the Life-saver around us, we may have to bob in the water for a little while before being pulled to safety, but at least there is peace, even in the distressed state.

Do you believe peace is possible in your turmoil? It comes through learning how to mourn and be comforted, not just lash out. I have found that not many people know how to mourn well and be comforted. We all know how to be sad and depressed, but that is not the same as mourning.

Why mourn? Is there purpose in mourning?

Somewhere in the fog and aftermath of being delivered the devastating blow, these words emerge from Matthew 5:4:

"Blessed are those who mourn, for they will be comforted"

Is "Blessed are those who mourn" a phrase you also struggle with? It does not feel like a blessing when you are mourning. Thankfully, this verse is not telling us that there is some twisted blessing in feeling sad. It is, however, a word of encouragement for the one who is courageous enough to admit the level of pain and sadness they are feeling. It is encouragement for the one brave enough to take some time to express their feelings instead of burying them inside.

It is not a blessing to feel sad, but it is a blessing to feel. I am sure you have heard of leprosy. Leprosy is talked of in the Bible. The law required that those with the disease be quarantined outside the village because they were viewed as "unclean." According to the American Leprosy Missions, leprosy is a disease that is caused by bacteria that causes a loss of sensation or a loss of feeling. As a result, those with leprosy can injure themselves without knowing it and then the injury can become infected, resulting in the need for amputation. In the end, a total loss is required simply because the person could not feel.[3] Having the ability to feel is a blessing.

If we do not acknowledge our pain, we cannot receive comfort. If we never allow ourselves to be comforted, we miss out on the intimacy of relationship that is built from navigating difficult situations together. In that one sentence, *blessed are those who mourn*, Jesus is encouraging us to feel. He is encouraging us to allow ourselves the opportunity to deeply experience the emotional peaks and valleys in whatever situation we find ourselves. He knew the importance of allowing ourselves to feel. Jesus knew that there is something rich and medicinal about mourning.

Jesus, who was there in the beginning when the world was formed, mourned while He was here on the earth He created. He knows everything – He is God – yet He mourned. He knows what is down the road – what is on the other side of the mourning - yet He still lived in the moment.

In John 11, when Lazarus died and Jesus knew that He was going to raise Lazarus from the dead, why do you think He wept before He raised him to life again? Why didn't He spare himself the sadness and just fix the situation? I think it is because He cared for those who were grieving. Mourning is an acknowledgement of the importance of what was lost. Jesus was always reminding us of what has real value. In His mourning, He demonstrated the value of Lazarus's life. He willingly entered into their pain before He brought the miracle.

Do you think Jesus weeps with you each month that you experience a death – the death of the hope for life? You better believe He does. Do you think He wept with you over the loss of your unborn child? Absolutely He did/does. If you have had to say goodbye to a little one much too soon, I am so sorry. Your loss is inexplicably great. I hope you know that Jesus is mourning right along side you because He cares for you. He doesn't mourn with despair as we may be prone to do. He mourns because our hearts are hurting, and He acknowledges the value of what was lost. He mourns with you.

We know that mourning is a part of this side of heaven. Our world has not yet been made new. God is at work, making all things new even as we speak, but the finished product has not yet been realized. One day every tear will be wiped from every eye, but in the meantime, we live in a world that has suffering. So how can we mourn well?

Weeping and mourning have less to do with feeling sad and depressed and more to do with expressing the emotion that naturally arises during a difficult situation. Sadness is naturally present, but in healthy mourning sadness is not unaccompanied. There is a complicated mix of emotions swirling around inside, but somewhere in the mix of healthy mourning is also hope. To mourn well is to acknowledge the pain for a season so you can move on wholly and healthily in due time.

In Jewish culture (Jesus's culture), when someone experiences a death, here is what happens: Immediately following the burial, those close to the deceased (parent, child, spouse or sibling) return to a home called the "shiva house." Here they begin a seven-day period of intense mourning. These mourners remain together in the house for the entire week without leaving the house. No one expects them to do anything other than mourn and reflect on the life that was lost. Their family, friends and neighbors take care of the needs of the mourners, freeing the mourners from having to leave the house and put on a "public face." The shiva is a deeply personal time of reflection, thus the mourners are removed from everyday life and given a period of time to begin dealing with their loss. After the 7 days are over, the mourners leave the house and are gradually re-introduced back into their normal life, but there are still a few restrictions for the next 23 days. When 30 days have passed, the time of mourning is officially over.[4]

This custom is beautiful in that during the time of mourning, everyone else in your community knew how to treat you and knew what to expect from you. The grieving were commanded to follow this custom so that they were given time to deal with their loss. It was believed that if the loss is never dealt with, a person is unable to move forward in wholeness and health.

So maybe you need to take a moment right now to reflect on whether or not you have allowed yourself to mourn your loss. If you have had a miscarriage or had the excruciating experience of holding your stillborn child in your arms you have not only experienced the loss of a hope, you have experienced the loss of a life. That life was no less significant than the loss of someone you knew well and with whom you could talk. Let me say that again. The life you lost is a life that must be mourned. Do not feel silly for mourning as you would mourn a parent or a sibling or a friend. The hole in your day-to-day life may not be as noticeable because the life you are mourning has never sat in a physical space next to you or altered how you do life on a day-to-day basis. However, the hole that it leaves in your heart is every bit as significant. Don't miss out on the important step of mourning that loss because you have believed the lie that your loss cannot compare to those who have lost an already-born loved one. A loss is a loss. There is no scale.

Then there is the loss you experience each month that your period comes. There may not be an actual physical life attached to that loss, but the loss is real. It is the grief over a hope for life. Every month that went by without the fulfillment of my hope and desire, I often wished there was a clear guideline for how to deal with my grief. I struggled because it was not as if I had actually lost someone – it was just the loss of the hope of someone. I felt depressed due to my circumstances, and, as we talked in earlier chapters, my hormones were also contributing to feeling depressed. Did that mean that I had no choice but to be miserable?

Mourning well

About a year and a half into my season of desiring baby number two, the Lord used the knowledge of the Jews' mourning custom as an opportunity to teach me about mourning. He used their custom to help me walk more victoriously rather than being completely taken out, as I had experienced each month prior. It began with recognizing that I did not have to be a victim to how I was feeling. My hormones and circumstances were not leading me well. They were destroying me. I did not enjoy being in a funk so often, and I am sure it was wearing on those around me - namely, my husband. Even my daughter was perceptive enough at 2 and a half years old to notice me crying and immediately assume it was because I wanted a baby. Everyone knew this desire for a baby was taking me out. I did not want to live in a consistently depressed state, so I got to the point where I would allow myself the first day of starting my period as my day to mourn the loss of a hope. I would allow myself that one day, and no more, to be sad. After that one day, I committed to no more mourning for that month's loss of hope.

Instead of just feeling sad and dwelling on the fact that I was not pregnant, I also learned to use that first day a bit more productively. It was an opportunity to press in to God with my pain, with my questions, and with my weakness. As I began to set up boundaries, instead of allowing my emotions to run the show, I began to see more clearly. I was better able to discern whether or not my sadness was due to the loss of hope or if there were bigger issues to be dealt with, such as anger with God or doubting His character and nature. As months pass by, the pain can add up, and the foundation of trust that we may have had with God at the beginning of our journey can begin to crack under the weight of the monthly beatings if the pain and disappointment are not dealt with.

Maybe you have been stronger than I was. If so, I am truly thankful on your behalf. It may even seem silly to you that I had to take a period of time each month to mourn the loss of a hope. Having the same level of grief and struggle is not a requirement for understanding each other on this journey. I know you have experienced grief, at least at some level, or you would not be reading this book. The purpose of this chapter is to give you the opportunity to examine whether or not you have allowed your heart to truly mourn, in a healthy way, during this season. If you have, then you have allowed yourself the freedom to move forward with a renewed hope and trust in God. If you have not yet mourned the loss(es) you have experienced, mourning may be a necessary step before you can cling hard to the truth you so desire.

So how long should you mourn? How long does it take for the acknowledgement of pain (which is healthy) to turn to despair (unhealthy)? The answer is different for everyone. The answer is different for each situation. There are no clear guidelines for how to mourn the loss of something hoped for. You and God are the only ones who know how long you can mourn your loss each month without it turning to despair. The second time I faced infertility and longing for a child for years, I learned not to park my mind on the loss, but instead to focus on whether or not I was trusting God and trusting the way He wants to write my story. I no longer allowed myself that day to mourn. The first time around, giving myself a day was better than letting my emotions run wild and spending the month in mourning, but the second time around, I realized that having a whole day to mourn was still an attempt to hold on to the disappointment rather than learning to let the disappointment go. I still acknowledged my disappointment. I still cried sometimes. Sometimes I cried quite a bit. But I also knew deep down that the more I poured my energy into surrendering every aspect of my life to Him (including children), the more peace I would have. Also, I found there is greater peace in watching God's story unfold, if I have allowed my heart to let go of my own plans. We really have little control over when and how God wants to build our family. If we are surrendered to Him, we are better able to see how He is leading us in this area, and we are more freed to enjoy the many other facets of life.

If you pull away from God, you will find that despair is waiting at your doorstep the minute you start your period or get the bad news. If, however, you fight to keep your focus on God throughout the month, a time of mourning *can be* a healthy initial response. Each day, all of us carry a little bit of the grief that accompanies an unfulfilled longing, but we know that some days are harder than others. Just do not let yourself be the victim of despair. It will not serve you well. Choosing to stubbornly believe in God's goodness that transcends circumstances will truly save you.

When we boil it down, at the heart of our mourning is a wish that things were different. After all, if things were different, there would be no reason to mourn. All would be well in our world. So how about this: Rather than focus on what you wish was different, try focusing on what God is doing around you right now and let that piece of the puzzle (what you long for) fall into place at the proper time. In the meantime, embrace the lessons He has for you in this moment. God promises to use all things for the good of those who love him (Romans 8:28). He does not bring the suffering, but He promises to teach us through it. He may want to teach you how to mourn because, like me, you had never had to truly mourn before. He may be strengthening your spiritual muscles to have the strength to cling to Him through any storm. He may be working to create greater levels of intimacy with people in your life. After all, this life is not about us. It is about Him. Life is about learning who

God is, learning how to have intimacy with Him, allowing Him to use our lives to show the world who He is, and learning how to love others well.

Mourn with those who are mourning...

> Jesus says, *"Rejoice with those who rejoice.*
> *Mourn with those who mourn"* (Romans 12:15).

These two commands are intricate pieces to the puzzle of learning how to love well and experience authentic fellowship with one another. When we are in the thick of our own grief, it is incredibly difficult to rejoice with others and even mourn with others. Both opportunities require giving your attention and focus to the other person and not directing it on yourself. You may be surprised to find it is a welcome relief to take the focus off your own troubles and enter into someone else's for a while.

In school, you may have learned the difference between the two words sympathy and empathy:

sympathy- to have feelings of pity and sorrow for someone else's misfortune.
empathy- to have the ability to understand and share the feelings of another.

Sympathy recognizes another's suffering whereas empathy recognizes *and shares* in the suffering. When God says to mourn with those who are mourning, He is not calling us to sympathy. He is not asking us to merely acknowledge a person's pain, He is inviting us to experience it right alongside them.

Maybe you are thinking, *that does not sound like much fun. Why would God encourage us to get sad on purpose? Isn't it enough to acknowledge that someone is hurting? Do we really need to hurt with them?* We certainly have a choice. We can watch from the sidelines, or we can get involved in the game. If we choose the more difficult road, the return is far greater.

Let's remember the story of Lazarus again. Jesus knew the story would not end in death, but still He wept. He allowed himself to be moved deep within. It did not matter what the future held. In the present moment, He saw the grief of the people, and He mourned *with them* because He loved them. When those we love hurt, we hurt. Jesus modeled this perfectly.

Jesus modeled empathy. In school, I was incorrectly taught that in order to have empathy, you have to have the same, or similar, experience as another person. That is not true. In order to have empathy for someone, you just need to have the ability to understand and the willingness to enter into their grief. Having this ability comes easier if you have been through something similar, but having shared experiences is not the only means to true empathy. The Bible says in Proverbs 20:5,

"The purposes of a man's heart are deep waters,
but a man of understanding draws them out."

The heart of a person is complicated and deep. If we are willing to take the time to understand, we are able to see and experience the heart of another. No two people will respond exactly the same in a given situation. It takes intentionality, through listening and asking questions, to learn and understand how the person in front of you is handling his/her situation.

To seek understanding means to ask questions, not offer answers. I think that is worth repeating. To love well and seek understanding means that you ask questions, not offer solutions. It takes practice to become good at asking questions. You do not have to get it right the first time; you just have to try. Try to understand. Don't jump to your own conclusions about their story or about their pain. Think about the people in your life who have been the most supportive and helpful through your grief. What did they do? What did they NOT do?

Practice makes perfect. Love rewards effort. Remember, we are no substitution for God when someone is dealing with grief, but we can be used by God to point others to Him. In the process, there is blessing for us. When we are able to get our own struggles and issues out of the picture for the moment, we are able to embrace the moment when someone else needs us. The following truths are good to store away in your heart regarding this topic:

"Do unto others as you would have them do unto you."

(known as the Golden rule – found in Matthew 7:12)

"Do nothing out of selfish ambition or vain conceit, but in humility consider others better than yourselves. Each of you should look not only to your own interests, but also to the interests of others" (Philippians 2:3-4).

Don't get so caught up in your own situation that you forget that there are people in your life going through their own struggles. Don't just look to your own interests. Look to the interests of others. Consider others more than you consider yourself. In doing so, you will safeguard yourself from falling into the pit of despair.

We have to be patient with our friends and family as they have the opportunity to grow in this skill of mourning with us. You do not have to surround yourself only with people who know exactly how you are feeling from personal experience. Remember: The ability to empathize is in all of us, but it is a difficult skill to learn. The key is in a person's willingness. If your friend is willing to walk this road with you, let them. The most comforting thing a dear friend, who was a mother of 5, said to me during one particular month of mourning was, "I don't know how to mourn with you, but I want to. I am sad with you." She had never been through the same struggle as me, but she felt my pain and desired to weep with me. If you do not have anyone in your life who is willing or able to express these sentiments to you as you mourn, you have one in Heaven who has already been mourning with you. He will mourn with you for however long this road is for you.

Rejoicing with those who are rejoicing in the very thing we are mourning...

I first wrote this book 7 years ago as I was in the thick of hoping for our third child. As I was writing this chapter, I wrote of the following experiences:

For the last three months, the circumstances surrounding the start of my period have given me opportunities to grow in character. Four months ago, I started my period and then headed off to co-host a baby shower. The next month, I started my period, then headed off to yet another baby shower. The following month, I started my period, then headed up to the hospital to meet my new nephew. Until recently, it had been over a year since I had been to a baby shower or held a newborn baby. Now here I was with two baby showers and a birth in three consecutive months and I started my period right before every event! I did not have to go looking for reminders about babies during my time of struggle, there was no avoiding them. Was the timing a blatant attack by the enemy? Can the enemy alter the start of my period? Did God have his hand in the timing? I don't have definitive answers for these questions, but what I do know is that all three scenarios offered an opportunity for me to die to myself. All three scenarios were not about me. They were times of celebration for someone else, but the enemy wanted to make the story about me. He wanted me to choose selfishness.

Normally, it is not difficult to celebrate with someone else. Celebrating is fun, whether it's for birthdays, anniversaries, promotions, success stories, etc. The key to celebrating well is to remember who the celebration is about. Therefore, any celebration is dampened when jealousy enters the picture. That is because jealousy is hungry for attention. Jealousy is not content to share. Jealousy is only concerned with self. Jealousy is impatient – it wants the object of its affection now. Jealousy feels better if no one else is able to have what it wants. Jealousy does not have a trusting bone in its body. Jealousy feels the need to take control.

We sometimes do not see the seriousness of letting jealousy dwell in our hearts, but God shows us that jealousy is even more devastating and damaging than anger and fury.

> *"Anger is cruel and fury overwhelming,*
> *but who can stand before jealousy?"* (Proverbs 27:4).

Jealousy is worse than anger and fury, which are described as cruel and overwhelming. Do not be overcome by the evil of jealousy, but overcome evil with good.[5] Overcome evil with love.

In contrast to jealousy, love is patient and kind. Love does not envy. Love does not think about itself. Love trusts. Love rejoices with truth[6]. Love is able to celebrate with someone regardless of how the celebration affects them. Love remembers that this life is not about self, it is about the Maker of all things and the other people He has made. If you are able to crucify your jealousy, celebration is made easier. Love, when substituted for jealousy, paves the way for strong relationships and greater joy.

Sometimes choosing love over jealousy has to be 100% a choice, but other times, our genuine love for a person can actually work as a safeguard against becoming jealous. Love is able to assist us in being able to celebrate with someone else, even in the very thing we long for ourselves. We love others well because God first loved us. Without God, it is impossible to love well. We will always love ourselves first and hurt others in the process if left to our own abilities. If we genuinely seek after the heart of God, a flowing spring of love for others begins to well up in us.

The Lord knows how many opportunities you have had to learn to die to yourself. He knows you have had to practice the skill of *rejoicing with those who are rejoicing* each time someone reveals the news that they are pregnant. When someone's cause for celebration is the very thing you have been longing for, it is natural to struggle in celebrating with the person. It is difficult, even painful. This is why it is called "dying to yourself." You have to momentarily set aside, or bury, your own desires for the sake of someone else. Jesus did this. You and I know that if Jesus was only thinking of Himself, He would not have died on the cross.

Jesus taught on this topic of "dying to ourselves." Matthew 16:24, Mark 8:23, and Luke 9:23 all record Jesus as saying, *"If anyone would come after me, he must deny himself and take up his cross and follow me."* Luke adds, *"he must deny himself and take up his cross **daily** and follow me"* (emphasis added). If we want to be like Jesus (who was the only perfect human to ever live), we have to learn how to deny ourselves. Later, Jesus goes on to say, *"And anyone who does not carry his cross and follow me cannot be my disciple"* (Luke 14:27). This idea of dying to ourselves, or denying ourselves, is critical to what it means to be a follower of Jesus. There is something pure and holy about willingly setting aside your desires or resources for the sake of someone else. It just feels good and right. That does not mean it is easy, but once the choice is made, life and freedom follow. There is a deep, rich goodness that fills us when we die to ourselves for the sake of someone else.

You have a choice. You can hold on to your grief, or you can let it go - which opens the door to freedom. The choice is entirely yours to make. Choose wisely.

God offers us a promise in Psalm 126:5-6: *"Those who sow in tears will reap with songs of joy. He who goes out weeping, carrying seed to sow, will return with songs of joy, carrying sheaves with him."*

To "sow" is to plant. If you plant a good seed, it will produce a life-giving plant. If you plant a bad seed (like a weed) it will steal nutrients and can kill the good plants you have sown. You can plant good seeds by thinking of others, even in your time of grief. The bad seeds are planted when we turn inward and focus on ourselves. Those who are inward focused do not "go out" with seed to sow. They are too consumed with their struggles to see the needs of those around them. *Those who sow in tears will reap with songs of joy.* We do not have to cover up our pain to sow good seeds in the lives of those around us. We have to be mindful and look to give more than we look to receive.

Feel free to be honest and call it like it is. You do not have to pretend you are as happy for them as you would be if you had the same news, but also recognize that the only thing holding you back from genuine joy on their behalf (good seed) is your own jealousy (bad seed). Which seed will you tend to and help grow?

I weep with grief...I have chosen to be faithful.

It is a tough road. There is no way around it. That is why the following verse became my prayer. Psalm 119:28-30 says:

"I weep with grief; encourage me by your word. Keep me from lying to myself; give me the privilege of knowing your law. I have chosen to be faithful; I have determined to live by your law."

When I was finally pregnant with my son, Joshua, I kept hearing the word "joy." When I say I "heard" the word joy, I mean that it was constantly on my mind whenever I would think about my unborn son. It was usually the first word that would pop into my head when I thought about him or felt him move. I did not know why I was hearing this word, so I would pray for joy. I would pray for Joshua to have joy. I felt like joy was God's word for him. Wouldn't you know it, the kid practically came out smiling. He smiled at an early 4 weeks old and has never stopped. He giggles and laughs far more than the average kid. His precious cheeks are complete with two dimples that add to the glee in his expression. He is joy in flesh. God had spoken to me, in my inner being, and assured me that joy would come from my mourning. I could not have imagined what the fulfillment of that promise would look like, but I chose to believe God would bring joy from my mourning. He promises that for you too, friend.

Joy comes in the mourning. Joy breaks through the pain like the early morning sun on the horizon if you allow yourself to feel and you take your feelings to your Maker. If you are strong enough, you may even be able to thank the Almighty for the opportunity to learn to rejoice with those who are rejoicing and to mourn with those who are mourning. You can know that you are mourning well if at any moment you are able to pause and acknowledge honestly that you trust God and you believe He is good. If you do not feel you are mourning well, God promises to help us in our weakness and to assist us when the task of rejoicing seems insurmountable due to our own mourning taking place.

He is our everlasting light – even when our circumstances seem so dark.

> *"Your sun will never set again, and your moon will wane no more;*
> *the Lord will be your everlasting light,*
> *and your days of sorrow will end"* (Isaiah 60:20).

Turn your face to the Light and let His light shine into those dark places of your heart that carry grief. Allow Him to heal you and receive His offering of peace.

Celebrating and genuinely sharing in another's joy and learning to mourn with those who are mourning are skills that must be practiced. Naturally, we are bent toward celebrating that which benefits us and mourning that which hurts or offends us. It is not natural for us to feel as joyful for someone who just got sent a hundred dollar check in the mail as we would be if that check had come to our mailbox, yet, that is precisely what God asks us to do. It is equally unnatural for us weep over the loss of a friend's mother as if we had lost our own mother, but this is what Jesus modeled for us.

The Creator of the Universe came to earth to take the form of a human and He had reason to weep. He knew everything. He knows everything. He knows how it will turn out in the end. He knows the deeper purposes behind why things are happening the way they are happening, and yet He still weeps over the matters of the heart that trouble us most. He weeps with us. It is okay to feel deeply.

Notes:

[1] Romans 12:15

[2] Matthew 5:4

[3] "leprosy," "Leprosy Frequently Asked Questions," *American Leprosy Missions*, http://www.leprosy.org/leprosy-faqs (accessed January 4, 2013).

[4] Mrs. Lori Palatnik, "ABCs of Death & Mourning," *aish.com*, http://www.aish.com/jl/l/dam/ABCs_of_Death_Mourning.html?tab=y (accessed January 4, 2013).

[5] Romans 12:21

[6] 1 Corinthians 13:4-8

Chapter 10

Power of Praise

"He has sent me (Jesus)...to bestow on them a crown of beauty instead of ashes, the oil of gladness instead of mourning, and a garment of praise instead of a spirit of despair. They will be called oaks of righteousness, a planting of the Lord for the display of his splendor." [1]

"From the lips of children and infants you have ordained praise because of your enemies to silence the foe and the avenger." [2]

---

30 chances to die to myself

When we were on our first round of infertility, I had over 30 opportunities to grow in character as I learned how to die to myself and rejoice with those who were rejoicing as each person I knew shared that they were pregnant. I had over 30 opportunities to decide how I would respond to the fact that I had not gotten what I so deeply desired. The greatest lesson learned during that time of character growth was the power and importance of praise.

"From the lips of children and infants, you have ordained praise because of your enemies, to silence the foe and the avenger."[3]

Praising God silences the enemy of your soul. You are God's child, the one with the power to silence the enemy.

We already talked about some of the enemy's tactics. He will try to isolate you, making you feel alone in this journey. He will get you to doubt the goodness of God's heart and even lie to you about the true nature of God's heart. He will make you feel like a failure as a woman because you haven't been able to carry a child. He will suggest you feel bad for yourself and turn inward. He will work overtime on your thoughts, to keep you from clinging to truth. This is always the goal of the enemy, but it seems he works overtime on the woman who is trying to conceive. He kicks you while you're down, so to speak. He hates life. He hates that as women we bear life. That is why we desperately need help silencing our enemy. The power that is unleashed, when we praise the One who is worthy of praise, brings instant silence to the enemy.

Here is the kicker. When we feel sad, weary or depressed, one of the last things we *feel* like doing is praising. In these times, praising takes effort. It takes mustering up the willpower to do so. If we are trying to get the gumption to praise because we think we *should*, we will seldom do it. On the other hand, if we recognize the spiritual battle that is always ensuing in the heavenly realms, and we see praise as our defense against the enemy, we might have a little more motivation to fight back, instead of being trounced on. In this case, letting your anger (at the enemy) drive you is a good thing. The enemy's biggest tool is the lies and deception that he stealthily worms into our hearts. If we can silence him, we take away his greatest weapon. If you were in a real, physical combat, it would be a no brainer to disarm your opponent if you had the opportunity. In doing so, you would take away the potential of being harmed by this opponent. Spiritual battle plays by the same rules.

I remember one particular weekend when I was driving up to Grand Rapids, MI to have an overnight with some of my college girlfriends. That morning I had started my period, so the last thing I wanted to do was be around people. I just wanted to mope around, feeling sad. Since this was a rare event that the girls were getting together, I did not want to cancel. I did not want to go and be depressed, so I resolved to do some serious warfare on my way up there. I cranked the music up loud and I remember pounding, yes pounding, my left foot on the floor so hard I was sure I would push a hole right through the floor of my car. As my foot was working like a jackhammer to the beat of the music, I was "singing" the words to the praise songs as loud as I could. As I did this, I became a hazard on the road because the tears were flowing from my eyes. As I listened to the words and fought to declare the truth of them over my life, my heart began moving from hardness and depression toward a moldable softness.

You see, the enemy preys on our weakness. When we give in to despair and wallow there, we are like stagnant water waiting for mosquitoes to lay their eggs and hatch greater nuisances. When we cry out to God and declare praise to Him, even when it's the last thing our heart *feels* like doing, the enemy is silenced in an instant. In an instant. He can't stand the praises of the One true God – it is worse than nails on a chalkboard to him.

You see, the Bible tells us that Satan used to be beautiful. He grew proud because of his beauty and, as a result, he was banished from God's presence. He wanted to be like God. He wanted the worship that was due to God alone.[4] Thus, when God's children worship the True King, it is the most devastating thing we can do to the enemy. He simply cannot stand under the weight of the power of God that is unleashed when God's people worship. At the name of Jesus, every knee in heaven and on earth and under the earth must bow (Phil. 2:10). His very name is so powerful that every knee will bow – even those who do not choose to do so. When you offer praise to God, you completely silence the enemy. We simply cannot afford to remain silent ourselves.

Examining our heart

When we consider whether or not we can offer praise to God when emotionally (and sometimes physically) we are feeling so run-down, we can get insight into the true condition of our hearts. We have to reconcile the questions of: Is God worthy of praise only when it *feels* natural and easy to praise? Is praise merely a natural result of an overflowing feeling or is there something deeper to the call to praise?

What makes God worthy of praise? This is a good question to have a prepared answer for. That way, in the times when you do not feel lovey-dovey with your Maker, you can remember His goodness anyway. This is so important that I am going to encourage you to take some time right now to make a list of why he is worthy of praise. Just write whatever comes to your mind.

Did you make your list? If you did, congratulations! You might have just written a modern day psalm. If this was too difficult for you or you did not want to take the time right now, maybe David's words can help get your gears turning. As you read, let your heart decide if you can agree with David. If you pause on something you are not sure you agree with, take note of it before moving on. This will give you insight as to what matters need to be settled in your own heart – where the battle needs to be fought. I hope you are as encouraged as I am that David, known as a man after God's own heart, had to tell his soul to praise the Lord. Several times in Psalm 103, he commands his soul to praise.

"Praise the Lord, O my soul; all my inmost being, praise his holy name.
Praise the Lord, O my soul, and forget not all his benefits –
who forgives all your sins and heals all your diseases,
who redeems your life from the pit and crowns you with love and compassion,
who satisfies your desires with good things so that your youth is renewed
like the eagle's.

The Lord works righteousness and justice for all the oppressed.
He made known his ways to Moses, his deeds to the people of Israel:

the Lord is compassionate and gracious, slow to anger, abounding in love.

He will not always accuse, nor will he harbor his anger forever;

he does not treat us as our sins deserve or repay us according to our iniquities.

For as high as the heavens are above the earth,

so great is his love for those who fear him;

as far as the east is from the west,

so far has he removed our transgressions from us.

As a father has compassion on his children,

so the Lord has compassion on those who fear him;

for he knows how we are formed, he remembers that we are dust.

As for man, his days are like grass, he flourishes like a flower of the field;

the wind blows over it and it is gone, and its place remembers it no more.

But from everlasting to everlasting the Lord's love is with those who fear him,

and his righteousness with their children's children –

with those who keep his covenant and remember to obey his precepts.

The Lord has established his throne in heaven,

and his kingdom rules over all.

Praise the Lord, you his angels, you mighty ones who do his bidding,

who obey his word.

Praise the Lord, all his heavenly hosts, you his servants who do his will.

Praise the Lord, all his works everywhere in his dominion.

Praise the Lord, O my soul."

David talks to himself in the second person. He tells himself to praise God and then gives an argument as to why to praise God. Sometimes we need to have that inner dialogue, like David, and argue with ourselves and convince ourselves to do what is good and right.

Forget not his benefits, sister. In Christ, you have been permanently washed clean of your bad choices. He forgives *all* your sins. He is Healer. On the journey of infertility, you are seeking His healing power over your reproductive organs, but His healing is over ALL of you. He takes your life and makes it new. He gives you love and compassion. He satisfies your desires with good things – yes, He does. You desire a baby. That desire is not yet fulfilled, but how many countless other ways has He satisfied your desires? Reflect on that now. What are some scenarios you can recall where God fulfilled the desires of your heart? In what ways did He go above and beyond what you expected? Bill Johnson, a pastor in Redding, California, describes the lavishness of God and His extravagance in this way: He says, "Look at the sky. I mean, how much sky do we really need?" It is true. We did not need as much sky as God has given us, but oh how we love it. God does not hold back His love. He lavishes it upon us. How has God loved on you? In what ways has God answered your request with a response that was different than you expected, but you saw that it was good?

In the old testament, God's people (which is us) are always being told to *remember*. In Joshua 4, God tells Joshua to stack a pile of stones so that the people would remember that they had crossed the Jordan on dry land. Really, God? You think they could experience something so incredible, so miraculous, and still need a reminder? Yes. We forget. For some reason, it is easier to forget the good things, yet the bad things stick for life. We need to intentionally engage our memory, and when we do, we re-discover the faithfulness of God.

Maybe you need to start your own pile of stones. I have a friend who has a vase that she has been slowly filling with stones, each with something written on them in permanent marker. Each time she has a moment that needs remembering, she writes it on the stone. She can glance at her stones any time and remember God's faithfulness in each unique situation.

When we sit down and take the time to reflect on why God is worthy of praise, we remember how worth He really is. Something else happens, too. We begin to *want* to praise Him. I think you would agree that God, the Maker of the Universe, is worthy of praise. He is worthy to be acclaimed. He is worthy to be spoken of and bragged about. He is incredible. He is magnificent. He is indescribable. He is good. He is God.

Praise positions the eyes of your heart on God, not on yourself.

If you stare at yourself in the mirror, do you like **all** that you see? I don't either – not all of it. When we stare at ourselves spiritually, it is equally unproductive and unfulfilling. When we praise God, we are directing our eyes toward Him and off ourselves. When we clearly see Him, it is impossible to not like everything we see. So why don't we stare more often?

We get distracted.

This is why the author of Hebrews (Hebrews 12:2) urges us to:

"Keep your eyes fixed on Jesus, the author and perfecter of our faith."

Paul puts it another way (Colossians 3:2):

"Set your minds on things above, not on earthly things."

People say, "get your head out of the clouds." I would like to ask, "Why?" It's a nice view up there. Above the clouds, there is always sun (during daytime hours). You can see clearly. When we are under the clouds, we can lose sight of the beauty that we know exists. When we keep our eyes fixed on Jesus, our vision is perfect. We see things for the way they really are, not the way we feel about them or the way the enemy would twist them to have us see.

Set your minds on things above, not on earthly things...

What Jesus accomplished on the cross – things above.

Our childless state – earthly things.

The importance of loving people and their souls – things above.

Being jealous of what others have – earthly things.

Focusing on who God is and learning about Him in the Word– things above.

How the world/our circumstances want us to view God – earthly things.

Being thankful for all we have – things above.

Dwelling on what we don't have – earthly things.

Taking time to remember what God has done – things above.

Giving energy to a situation we wish was different – earthly things.

When you focus on the earthly things, you will feel your energy zapped. On the other hand, if your mind is fixed on things above, you are energized. When you spend your time thinking about God and things above, you will have less desire to dwell on earthly things. It is impossible to think about yourself when you are enthralled with the Maker of the Universe.

Back in 2012, I had the privilege of taking 40+ teenagers to a 27-hour youth event. The morning that we were going to leave, I noticed a little pink. My heart sank as I was really hoping this would be the month I would finally get pregnant. Due to the "training" that I received from the Lord over the prior few years, I instantly began crying out to God, asking Him to help me trust Him, to remain faithful to Him and to not fall into a depressed state. I wanted to remain faithful and joy-filled for myself and probably more so for the teenagers that I would be spending time with. If you have ever spent much time around teenagers, you know that they thrive on energy.

Over the following two days, I had a bit of cramping, but no more signs of the period until the evening that the event was coming to a close. At that point, I was fairly certain that I was not pregnant and that my period would ramp up at any moment.

Throughout the weekend, I had many thoughts like, *Why does this have to happen right now? This is the worst time as I am here with all these youth. I just want to go home and curl up on the couch in the fetal position. I don't want to have to push through this. I just want to be alone where I can deal.* In other words, I wanted to go home and be depressed. I did not want to have to fight.

I was only focused on the here-and-now and it seemed like this was the worst time to start my period.

Looking back, I can see it from a different perspective, from the heart of a loving Father. Processing the disappointment during a time when I needed to pour out my time and energy, was a difficult time to start. At the same time, being at a worship event was probably the best time to start because I had no choice other than to fight - if I did not want to completely fail in my role as a youth leader that weekend. I did not have the option of sitting and wallowing and being depressed. In addition, I was surrounded by an atmosphere of worship. I was being bombarded with truth from every angle. Could there be a more perfect place to be when you are battling spiritually (i.e. struggling with your emotions)? If a loved one was struggling, I would want them to be surrounded by an atmosphere of love and truth. In the end, I handed in my resignation as author of my story and recognized that God knew better what the "perfect" time to start my period would be.

The reality was simple. That was not the month that God chose to create a life in me. I could not do anything to change or alter that. I could be frustrated and sad that things did not go my way, or I could CHOOSE to trust God and let Him do with my life what HE would like to do with my life. After all, a life spent following Jesus is a life of surrender. It is the voluntary laying down of one's life into the hands of another. It is saying to Jesus, "My life is not my own. You may do with it what seems best to you."

Can you trust Him? He is trustworthy, but can YOU trust Him? He does not change. He is the same yesterday, today, and forever.[5] Your circumstances change, but He is the same no matter whether you are experiencing a wonderful day or a dreadful day. Therefore, He is worthy of praise always – on good days and bad days. When we worship Him on good days, our worship adds to our joy and peace and blesses the heart of God. When we choose to worship Him on the bad days, something extremely powerful happens. We engage in the battle that is always ensuing, and we refuse to back down. We refuse to be defeated.

Let me share with you an example of what this looks like lived out. Every year, I have committed to writing a Christmas letter to send to our friends and family. Every year, I feel compelled to sincerely share about our lives in a way that gives God the glory He deserves. Some years this is easy. Other years, it is more difficult. What I have realized, is that God has used our most trying seasons to touch people's lives (including ours) the most. I am going to allow you a window into our world. I want to share our Christmas letter from when we were in the thick of our first season of infertility. It is laced with the lessons God was teaching us at the time. Many of those lessons are here in this book. Here is our family's Christmas letter from 2008:

Hello!

"My pony's Misty," Alliyah would tell you. Yes, we officially have a new member of the family. Since Alliyah could walk, I secretly really wanted a pony for Alliyah so that she could learn to take care of it and have a horse her size

(since Alliyah is at Marcy's knee level). I kept thinking, "Some day, when we have a house on land, hopefully we can get Alliyah a pony." Well, at the end of the summer, we met a wonderful family who was going to rent to own our home (so we could pursue finding a home with land). It ended up not working out to have them rent our home, but through beginning a relationship with them, we now have a pony that was given to us, and I am helping them train their horse.

God knows the deepest desires of our hearts, and the Bible says, "If you delight yourself in the Lord, he will give you the desires of your heart." Misty is proof of that. We also know that this verse isn't a "money tree," so to speak – where you can wish it and it will happen. The biggest treasure when you delight in God is you get Him plus all the bells and whistles of a relationship with him. We have learned of this great gift this past year.

If we were to sum up the past year, we would use words like: "Waiting," "Hoping," and "Trusting." We believe what the Bible says that God has good plans for us, and this year, that belief has been tested. In the summer of 2007, we began a journey of trying to buy a major fixer-upper on 5 acres. This property already had a barn and pasture – the house just needed an overhaul. We began the pursuit of a dream: To have a home on land where we could keep our horse, Marcy (now, Misty, too!). Over the course of over a year, we almost had the house bought twice, but it slipped through our hands twice. The door was officially closed this past summer when someone else got their offer in a day or so before us. There was a lot of waiting, hoping, and trusting. We are still waiting, hoping, and trusting that one day we will have a place of our own on land with horses.

Another thing that we have been waiting, hoping, and trusting God about is our desire to have more children.   We began trying for #2 in June of 2007 (around the same time we thought our dream of a home on land might become a reality sooner than later).   As I write this, we are still on the journey of waiting, hoping, and trusting. I can't explain in words how extremely difficult this journey has been and yet, I can tell you that the lessons learned, the character-building, and the deepening trust in God have been far worth the suffering.

Over a year ago, we had two deep desires that we thought would be fulfilled quickly, yet to this day, we have not yet seen those desires fulfilled. We have been tempted on many occasions to wonder if God really cares about our desires – to wonder if he hears our many, many prayers offered about these two situations. Yet, this we know is true: God doesn't change. His love is the same yesterday, today, and forever. He does care, and He always hears. We have learned that a life lived in the pursuit of self-gratification is a miserable life, but a life lived for the sake of God and others is a joy-filled and peaceful life even amidst very tough situations.

Through the storm, we have seen a beautiful, compassionate heart growing in our daughter. Every month that I have found out I'm not pregnant has felt like a death. In the times when I've been sad, our precious little daughter has taken me in her arms and said, "Mommy, you sad? Brother, sister? It's okay, mommy. It's okay." Her heart is so compassionate. It is good to know how to mourn WITH other people, even when the hard situation isn't happening directly to you. This has been an extremely valuable lesson for us to learn as we are now better equipped to love our friends and family and to walk WITH them through the joys AND sorrows.

As we look forward to 2009, we remember that Jesus commands our destiny. We don't know what the future holds. We are still very hopeful that as we "delight in God, he will give us the desires of our hearts." We also know that God is the greatest treasure of all and we can't lose him. We also know that we have already received so much: God's love, his forgiveness, a warm home full of clothes and other goodies, plenty of great food to eat, etc. On top of all that, we have so many wonderful family members and friends. We are so thankful for you. We pray that you all know how deeply loved you are during this Christmas season.

Love, Todd, Jillian, Alliyah and Emma (cat), Marcy (horse) and Misty (pony)

(We look forward to adding more names here!)

The following year, in our 2009 letter, I was able to express God's goodness from the other side - the side where our desires were fulfilled. Both letters and both seasons were valuable and it was important to cling to the goodness of God through both seasons. Here is a portion of what I wrote in our Christmas letter:

Blessed: "To make supremely happy"
Blessing: "A thing conducive to happiness"
Favor: "Gracious kindness, friendly regard shown by a superior

During our "desert year" of 2008, we learned about the Favor of the Lord that goes deeper than anything material. It is no coincidence that Alliyah's favorite song, since she could sing and still to this day, has been "Blessed Be the Name of the Lord." If you've never heard the song, the verses remind us that the Name of the Lord is blessed (makes us supremely happy), both when things are good and when things are bad. This song has been a good life song for us over the last couple years. The truth is: God is worthy of our praise. Period. His praiseworthiness has nothing to do with our circumstances or how we feel toward him. He is good and though we don't always understand our circumstances, his goodness doesn't change.

This is the truth. God's favor is upon YOU, too, whether or not you can recognize it. He has been "gracious and compassionate to you, slow to anger, but abounding in love" (Psalm 86:15). "He has not treated you as your sins deserve" (Psalm 103:10). He has given you friendly regard even though you deserve the cold shoulder. AND when you simply acknowledge His goodness (as we all should do anyway), He tacks on the benefit of allowing you victory over your enemy. This is good news! Fight hard!!

"Great are the works of the Lord; they are pondered by all who delight in them. Glorious and majestic are his deeds, and his righteousness endures forever. He has caused his wonders to be remembered; the Lord is gracious and compassionate" (Psalm 111:2-4).

Here are a list of praise and worship songs I recommend warring with:

...Some of them are oldies, but they're goodies! 😌

Blessed Be the Name of the Lord – Passion
I Will Not Be Shaken – Jadon Lavik – THIS IS PROBABLY MY FAVORITE!!!
You Never Let Go – Matt Redman
Praise You in This Storm – Casting Crowns
Unchanging – Chris Tomlin
From the Inside Out - Hillsong
Voice of Truth – Casting Crowns
All I Really Want – Lincoln Brewster
The Only Name - Big Daddy Weave
We Won't Be Shaken - Building 429
Good Good Father - Chris Tomlin
Run to You - Kari Jobe
Greatness of Our God - Natalie Grant
Your Love Never Fails - Newsboys
Help Me Find It - Sidewalk Prophets
East to West – Casting Crowns
Enough – Chris Tomlin
It is Well With My Soul – Jars of Clay or Bethel Music
Healer – Ten Shekel Shirt
Lord Reign In Me – Brenton Brown
Trading My Sorrows – Darrell Evans
Once Again – Matt Redman
Hosanna – Paul Baloche
Mighty To Save – Hillsong
Draw Me Close – Kelly Carpenter
Everlasting God – Lincoln Brewster

Add your own...

Notes from Chapter 10:

_____

[1] Isaiah 61:3

[2] Psalm 8:2

[3] Psalm 8:2 NIV, 1984 edition.

[4] Ezekiel 28:12-19, Isaiah 14:12-15.

[5] Hebrews 13:8

Chapter 11

The Chapter for the Man

"A loving doe, a graceful deer- may her breasts satisfy you always, may you ever be captivated by her love." [1]

"The purposes of a person's heart are deep waters, but one who has insight draws them out." [2]

The desire for a child can draw you closer or drive you apart. You choose.

I love the following verse: *"Words kill, words give life; they're either poison or fruit - you choose"* (Proverbs 18:21 MSG).

In the same way that the words we choose to use can either poison or bring forth life, this road of desiring a child can either be like poison to your marriage or it can serve to bring more life, more intimacy, more "fruit" to your marriage. It's a choice. Your words (or lack of words) are a part of that choice. Will you choose to be more closely united with your spouse, or will you choose to withdraw?

The enemy of your soul wants to poison your marriage with this struggle in desiring a child. He will try to drive a wall between you and your spouse. Written on the wall are things like: *"You don't understand me." "I don't feel we are in this together." "I have to go through all of this stuff and you don't have to do anything." "Sex is a duty – a means to an end." "Why don't you just chill? We will get pregnant eventually."* The enemy will try to increase your stress and steal your joy. He will try to get each of you to look only to your own interests, forgetting to consider how this journey is affecting your spouse. He will attack your sex life. You can choose to fall prey to this enemy or you can choose to fight.

So, men, this chapter is for you. Whether you and your beloved have been united on this journey or you are having a difficult time navigating this path together, I thought it might be helpful for someone else to help you understand how your woman is doing. I also hope to illuminate a few of the struggles that are unique to you as men. It will be up to the two of you to speak up when a portion of what you read hits home personally. I hope you have been able to read through this book together, but if this is the only chapter you read, please take the time to talk together about what God is doing in each of your hearts, seeking to truly understand how the other is feeling and coping.

You don't understand.

As described in chapter 7, you guys cannot "get" the way we feel because you have not experienced what we have experienced. You don't have tickets to ride on the same hormonal roller coaster that we get to ride every month. It is helpful to keep this in mind when that unwelcome visitor comes knocking, bringing with her all of the baggage of bloatedness and discomfort. In addition, Aunt Flo brings the horrific news that declares with every change of the pad or tampon, "You're not pregnant!" Guys cannot understand how a woman can be seemingly fine one minute and then go to use the bathroom, emerging with a renewed sense of despair over whether or not she will ever experience the joy of carrying a child inside her womb. Our emotions can take a dive that quickly, and it often catches our men off guard simply because they have never experienced it for themselves.

There is no question that men and women are different and, therefore, our responses to situations will be different. Even two women will respond differently to the same situation. The key is not to generalize all women or all men, but to get to know your woman or your man.

Some men generalize women. They lump us all into this box with the outer label saying things like: "Emotional, Controlling, I can never understand her, so why try..." Too many men give up before they have put forth a good effort to get to know their woman. The result is a disconnected, unsatisfying relationship. The first step toward a mutually satisfying relationship is to admit where you may have stereotyped your woman. The following is a list of stereotypes that often get applied to women. See if you are guilty of assuming most (if not all) women are like this:

- Controlling
- Emotional

- Hormonal
- Demanding
- Needy
- Clingy
- Weak
- Talk too much
- Not as smart
- Cannot drive well (If someone fails to use their blinker, and it happens to be a woman, my husband jokingly says something like, "Did you notice who was driving?")

Now let's look at some of the stereotypes about men:

- Have no feelings/Stoic
- Backing down from a fight shows weakness
- Impenetrable
- No deep thoughts
- Helpless without a woman
- Crying is a sign of weakness
- Self-sufficient
- Talking about issues shows weakness

Each of these labels is a lens you choose to look through. Unfortunately, all of these lenses will, in some way, distort the way you see your wife (or your husband). If you assume all women are controlling, then you project onto your wife that she is controlling. If she makes a suggestion for where to go to dinner, you may throw her suggestion into that compartment that proves she is controlling instead of valuing her input. You will see each situation where she offers an opinion as her trying to control. As another example, let's look through the "emotional" lens. If your wife is sad over something, you may not take her seriously. You may write her off as being emotional instead of pursuing her and getting to the bottom of what may be making her sad. Or you may take the passive route, deciding that, since she is sad way more often than you, she must just be "emotional."

These generalizations affect you men as well. Do you give yourself the freedom to express your feelings, your hurts, your frustrations? We know you have them. Have you given yourself the permission and the time to process how infertility is affecting you, or have you chosen to keep busy so you do not have to deal with those feelings? Believe it or not, most women respect their man a great deal more when they are able to open up and be vulnerable. God has given you a heart that feels deeply, but the enemy has tried to convince you to stuff those feelings under the guise of appearing strong.

Now is the time for both of you to pause and evaluate how your marriage, and thus your infertility journey, has been affected by these stereotypes.

You will treat a person in a manner that is consistent with what you believe about them. Is what you believe about your spouse accurate? Have you taken the time to really get to know her (his) heart? Do you know *why* your spouse is the way she (he) is? Do you know why your spouse wants a child so badly? Do you know why infertility has been so difficult for her (him)? Can you predict the bumps in the road that have the potential to take her (him) out? Do not settle for answering these questions with assumptions. Make sure you have talked with each other and truly understood each other on this journey.

Proverbs 20:5 says,

"The purposes of a person's heart are deep waters,
but one who has insight draws them out."

The older NIV version (1984) says, *"The purposes of a man's heart are deep waters, but a man of understanding draws them out."* Your woman's heart is a deep, deep well. You, better than any person on earth, have the opportunity to draw her out and understand her. The fact that you are a man and she is a woman does not provide a barrier preventing you from truly understanding her unless you let it. If we seek understanding, if we ask God for insight, we will understand the depths of one another's hearts. Men and women are different. That is no secret. So it makes sense that desiring a child will affect each of you differently, but that does not mean that you cannot be completely united in heart and in mind as you walk this path together. Attaining understanding will not come without hard work. You may think you understand, but if your wife does not feel understood, then you do not understand, and a quest for greater understanding is necessary.

It took a year and a half before my husband and I were walking together on this path. I had been months into the cloud of depression and despair before it occurred to him that we were having a problem getting pregnant. Once his eyes were opened, I thought he and I would mourn together and seek answers together. This was not the case. He did not feel the need to mourn, like I did. The fact that we were not yet able to get pregnant was not affecting him the way it was affecting me, and that made me mad at him and it made me feel more alone. I shared my struggles with him, and he listened, but I never felt connected as a result of our conversations. What it came down to was, I did not feel understood, and I felt as if it was my responsibility to deal with my emotions and he would be there waiting when I figured it out. I did not want him waiting on the sidelines cheering me on. I wanted him to jump right into the pile of crap (my emotional turmoil) with me (empathy). I did not want him to look from the side and offer a hose when I was through wallowing in the poop (sympathy). He saw me being depressed and, although my poor mental state bothered him, he was not being affected by our circumstances in the same way I was. I was a wreck and it seemed like it did not bother him at all.

I actually started to think he had a problem. Maybe he just could not *feel* things. Maybe he needed help. Maybe. Or maybe he is just different and deals with things differently and maybe that is a good thing. What would our lives had been like if both of us were wallowing in depression? Had I really taken the time to understand him, instead of assuming he was in the wrong because he wasn't responding to the situation like I was?

Ahh. See it? The enemy was trying to drive a wedge between us because we were different. I thought I wanted him to feel the way I felt because then I would feel assured that I was not crazy. I would feel validated for feeling sad. I desperately wanted to not feel alone in my crap, and my husband did not know how to jump in there with me. We both needed to learn how to understand the other person and why our responses were so different. Deep down, I did not really want him to be affected the way I was. I just wanted to know that he understood my heart, saw my pain, and CARED. At the same time, I wanted to tangibly see that the desire for a child mattered to him, too.

You don't care.

Guys, you are not completely oblivious to the emotional swings a woman can experience. You have experienced emotional highs and lows. If you are a sports fanatic, then you know the thrill and adrenaline rush when your teams scores a goal, touchdown, makes a nice shot, or hits a home run. You also know the valley of sadness or anger when your team losses. This emotional attachment to a game played by people you do not even know is intriguing to me. My husband is a Detroit Tigers fan and when they lose, it has the potential to ruin his night. I do not get that. I have asked him why he has an actual emotional response to a game like that, and the best answer he has been able to give is that he feels invested in the game.

Maybe that is where the rubber meets the road here: Investment. A woman's emotional response to the hope and desire for a child is closely linked with the degree to which she has invested her time, energy, and thoughts. When we were desiring baby #2, I was invested – probably too invested. I already shared with you how the desire for a baby became consuming for me. I dedicated a good chunk of my mental energy to thinking about and desiring another child.

The second time around dealing with infertility was different. As we were nearly 2 years into a similar journey, I realized that my experience had been drastically different because of where I had chosen to invest. The situation was the same. We desired another child and we had been trying for close to 2 years without the fulfillment of the desire. The second season of desiring a child was filled with peace and joy and purpose; whereas, the first season was mostly filled with depression. The second time, I was able to put into practice the truth that God had taught me over the first 5 years of our infertility journey – truth I have shared with you in this book. As a result, life was not put on hold in order to wait for a child. I fought hard to choose to look for what God had on my plate EACH DAY. *"Tomorrow will worry about itself,"* said a very wise man (a.k.a. Jesus in Matthew 6:34).

So where are you investing individually and as a couple? Men, since this chapter is for you, how can you encourage your wife to be involved and mentally invested in the things that God has in front of her right now? How can you help her to free up some of her mental space to think about things other than desiring a child? A word of caution in doing this: Encouraging her to invest in the here and now does not mean that she does not get the space to talk about and think about her desire for a child. We are not encouraging avoidance – we are just encouraging a change in your mental investment portfolio.

Then the question begs to be asked. Men, what does your mental invest-ment portfolio look like? Have you allotted *any* of your mental energy to go toward this desire to have a child? I'm not asking if you are willing to pursue another child. I am asking if you are personally talking with God about your desire and your wife's desire to expand your family. I am asking if you are be-ing intentional about knowing her body and the changes and challenges that she faces throughout a month. This is not her cross to bear alone. It is easier for the man to check out because his body is not the one being affected. Once again, we come back to the importance of being intentional.

If you *have* allocated some of your mental investment portfolio to thinking about having a baby, does your wife know about it? Have you shared with her how you have been affected? Where are you struggling the most?

Men, we want your protection, we want your guidance, and we want to know you are with us. Our hearts are particularly vulnerable during this sea-son and part of our identity as women (life-bearers) is threatened. We want you to fight for us. We want to know we are not alone. In your heart, you may know that you care deeply, but if your woman is not feeling it, then some-thing is up. She wants to SEE that you care. Action.

You can choose to keep things status quo and let her work through her struggles on her own, or you can love her well, dying to yourself, doing what does not come natural to you, so she can experience more freedom. You might need to be intentional about telling her how you are feeling. Loving her well might be as simple as asking her how she is doing with this struggle or letting her know you see her pain today. She needs you. She wants you. It is fairly easy to let her know you care, you just have to do something. You have to be intentional.

Another example where you can let her know you care is with decision-making. With birth control, I hear too many men say things like, "It's up to her, it's her body." I don't mean to be rude, but I honestly think that is a lazy response. It requires no action on the part of the man and it shirks all of the responsibility onto the shoulders of the woman. In the case of desiring pregnancy, we are not talking about birth control, but we *are* talking about decisions that are being made that affect her body. If you pursue medical assistance, you both need to make the decisions about how far you are willing/able to go, and you can honor her by always keeping her safety, emotional and physical, in mind. Protect her in this process. Think about how each decision will affect her.

Pray!

Most importantly, pray for her.

> *"Isaac prayed to the Lord on behalf of his wife,*
> *because she was barren. The Lord answered his prayer,*
> *and his wife Rebekah became pregnant"* (Genesis 25:21).

Pray to the Lord on behalf of *your* wife.

Your prayers matter more than you may realize. They matter because somehow, mysteriously, they move the heavens. They matter because it means that you are willingly engaging in the spiritual battle that is being waged against your wife and against you as a couple. I do not even know you, but I would be willing to believe that there would be no question what your response would be if someone physically came after your wife. You would do everything you could to take that enemy out. Spiritually speaking, it is no different. Your wife needs you to go to bat for her. She needs you to kick some demon butt in the name of Jesus.

In addition to the battle being waged, Jesus urged us in Matthew 6:21 that *"where your treasure is, there your heart will be also."* Whatever you invest in, your heart will follow. If you are invested in praying for your wife and fighting for her, your heart will be drawn to her and she will see that she is not alone. She will tangibly know that the two of you are united in this journey. She will not feel as though she has to navigate the trail on her own. You are right there beside her and maybe even slightly ahead of her, holding her hand and helping guide her.

About Sex...

Disclaimer: Depending on where you are coming from, this portion of the chapter might be a little uncomfortable. I feel it is important to directly address the issue of sex, but I recognize that addressing the sexual union of a husband and wife can be a little awkward.

Sex should not be a chore or duty. When you are trying to have a baby, sex can easily become a means to an end as opposed to an intimate union. If you are pursuing medical intervention, sex might even be taken out of the equation of the actual conception. So what do we do with that?

My husband and I have wrestled a lot with this issue of sex, personally and with others. We have had the great responsibility of doing pre-marital counseling for a few couples and the sex talk is always the most dynamic. We have all been dramatically affected by our upbringing, experience, the media, and our peers when it comes to our view of sex.

I went to a personal shower for a bride-to-be and the shower was really a sex toy party. I knew what I was getting into, but I did not know what I was getting into, if you know what I mean. I am not embarrassed by talk of sex or sex toys, but as I sat there listening to the products, my soul was uneasy. As I sat back and listened to these beautiful women talk, I saw that these sex toys were designed with one thing in mind, the physical feeling. Unfortunately, almost every item offered was a substitute for the real thing. Now, I know that sex is a touchy subject, and I am by no means passing judgment here. However, I do want to pose some questions that I had to ask myself. Would I rather a machine make me feel a certain way or my husband? Even if my husband is in control of the machine, wouldn't it be more intimate for us if it was his hands touching me, not a machine? If my husband has not learned how to make sex a time of mutual enjoyment, will these "toys" actually bring the solution? If I feel the need to "spruce up" our sex life, is the problem with the physical or is there something deeper?

...take a deep breathe if that was a little uncomfortable to read.

We all come in to marriage with an idea and expectation about sex. We are all incredibly sensitive in this department, whether we are willing to admit it or not. We want to be good in bed. We want to love the other person well AND we want to enjoy it, too. If any of these wants or expectations are not met, we are a sitting duck, ready to be overcome by the enemy.

My husband grew up in a home where sex was not talked about. The only thing mentioned was, "don't do it." He never had "the talk" with his Dad. As a result, he grew up feeling like sex was wrong, taboo, and you do not talk about it. Then he married a girl who grew up without concrete standards and not a lot of experience, at least not good experiences. The mix led to a lot of misunderstanding, hurt, and frustration. Sex is just supposed to come easily, naturally, smoothly, right? The media has told us this lie, but the reality is that sex can be quite awkward and anything but smooth at first. If sex is an expression of a couple's intimacy, then it would make sense that it would take some time for things to work like clockwork.

Intimacy grows over time with intentionality and effort. I did not know how to encourage my husband perfectly when we first got married. I did not realize that I was hurting him in some ways. We had to talk things out, figure things out. Things do not work themselves out on their own. It takes intentionality, investment, and a willingness to grow and learn. Sex is no different.

We have seen that Satan does everything possible to push a couple together in sexual union before they are married and once they are married, he does everything he can to drive them apart, preventing them from coming together physically. How sad. We finally have all the guilt-free freedom in the world, and suddenly there are all these issues.

In case you struggle with having a good, godly perspective on sex, allow me to lay out the truth we have come to rest on.

Sex was God's design. In the workbook, <u>Preparing for Marriage</u>,[3] it says, "God's purposes for sex are: for procreation, pleasure, and protection." Ladies, we have a clitoris and it serves no other bodily function than to provide women with pleasure during sex. God did not have to give us that "part." This proves he designed it to be pleasurable. We know it is pleasurable, but it is freeing to know that God is pleased when we are pleased. It is not a dirty thing.

He also designed that the intimate union requiring the man to literally enter into the woman would be the beautiful start of new life: Procreation. He designed that a part of the man be joined with a part of the woman and a new life would begin as a result. He said to Adam and Eve, *"be fruitful and increase in number"* (Gen. 1:28.). He encouraged and commanded them to come together to multiply. We do not need to address this issue any further. You and I both agree on this, or you would not be reading this book, and I would not be writing it.

Protection. Husbands, I pray that the breasts of your wives always satisfy you and you do not choose to look elsewhere for satisfaction. The satisfaction in your wife was God's intent, His perfect will. He gave you one woman, his beautiful daughter, to love and cherish as long as you live. Do not break this vow. We already talked about how most couples struggle with sex once they are married, so, if this is you, you are definitely not alone. At the same time, you have the power to fight hard for your marriage by fighting for a healthy sex life. If you are not coming together regularly, talk about why that is. Get to the heart of the matter, so that you can both be free. You have what it takes to love your wife well, in bed and out. Do not believe otherwise. It does not matter how far you have strayed, our God is a God of unity, and sex is the most powerful sign of unity. He will fight for you and alongside you. You need to fight, too. You have what it takes to see victory. Do not give up if you face opposition. And I beg you, do not look for satisfaction elsewhere – neither in the physical arms of another nor the imaginary arms of another (pornography).

There was a point in our marriage where it genuinely did not matter to me if we ever had sex again. I did not want it. Because of my husband's baggage from the past, he was not initiating, and I was quite alright with that. The Holy Spirit was not alright with that. Although I was okay with not having sex, I was also plagued with worries that Todd would have an affair. I felt stupid or shameful when friends would mention sex. I was not free. The Holy Spirit knew it and did a good work in us – causing us to hash things out and get to the heart of why we were not free. This hashing came in the midst of when we were having sex regularly because we were trying to conceive. The fact that we were having sex, did not mean we were healthy. I was having sex because I wanted a baby, not because I wanted to connect with my husband

and participate in something holy. My husband was happy because he did not need to initiate because it was "expected." He did not fear rejection.

So if you are not feeling good about your intimacy with your spouse, talk about it. Try to understand where the other person is at and fight to be healthy in this area.

Todd and I have committed to being honest with one another. He is honest if he is too tired to give it his best in bed. I am honest if I do not want to have sex. We have talked about things, so we both know that my admission that I do not have the desire is not a slammed door. I know that it is important to push past my lack of desire because it is important to come together with my husband. Marriage is not about just one person. I seek to die to myself because I *know* that our marriage is always under attack, and I want to keep us protected. So most of the time, during those times when I am struggling, I tell him, "I do not want to, but I do want to (because I know it's good and protects us)." He understands and does not feel rejected or undesirable because we have talked about it before that moment. In the end, I am always glad we came together.

You may not be able to relate to our story exactly. People have different stories, different sex drives. The fact remains that a man and a woman may be on different pages, different wavelengths, different sex drives, but as husband and wife, you are called to be united. It is important to evaluate whether or not the place you are at in your thinking/feelings about sex is born out of freedom or out of hurts and unhealthy things of the past.

Todd and I have committed to making sure sex is a natural overflow of our relationship in clothes. We have invested in each other, taking the time to know each other, enjoy being together, and having fun together. This is what we are like with clothes on, so that should naturally overflow into our sex life, but it does not come easy. It has not come easy. Trying to have a baby puts an added pressure on things. It is a myth that sex should just come easily. Few actually live in this reality. If you do, Hallelujah!! For the rest of us, sex is something we need to protect, be committed to, and seek to honor God with - both in our thoughts and in our actions.

What now?

You cannot make the miracle happen now, but there is something you can do. You can prepare for the day that God hands you your miracle by working on having a strong and healthy marriage now. One of the best pieces of advice I received was to always prioritize my spouse as second on the list, just under God, and above kids – yes, above kids. In making your spouse a priority, you are actually prioritizing your kids as well. They need a mom and dad who are healthy and love each other. They need a mom and dad who are united and strong. The best way you can love your future kids is to have a strong and healthy marriage, now and then. Here are a few "marriage strengthening" tools to keep in mind as you invest in your marriage now.

__Assume the best about your spouse__. Assume that his/her heart is good in whatever situation you find yourself. Another way of saying this would be to give your spouse the benefit of the doubt. In doing this, you save yourself a lot of time in defensive banter. Deep down, your spouse does not *want* to hurt you. The reality is that he/she does hurt you sometimes, but the desire of their heart is to bless you.

Here is an example that has come up in our home on numerous occasions. The dishes lay on the counter for the third day in a row. *He knows how much I hate doing dishes*, I think to myself. *We have agreed that this is his job. Why hasn't he done them yet?* I have a choice. I can choose to believe that my husband is lazy, that he is purposely not doing the dishes OR I can choose to believe that he has been busy and has prioritized other things first – other good things. One way of looking at the situation paints my husband in a bad light, the other paints him in a good light. We need to practice seeing our spouse in the best light possible. Give them the benefit of the doubt. It feels wonderful to be on the receiving end of someone having thought the best of you.

> *"Be devoted to one another in love.*
> *Honor one another above yourselves"* (Rom. 12:10).

*****Be your spouse's biggest advocate.** You may not always think highly of your spouse. Your spouse is, after all, human, but whenever you speak of him/her to others, paint them in the best light possible. There will always be someone helping point out the bad in others. Don't be that person. Be the one who says to the world, I love this man/woman because... I think so highly of this person because... Also, defend him/her to anyone that would oppose your spouse. If you were a defense lawyer, you would do your research on your client and the case in order to defend them as best as possible. The research you can do in your marriage is to come up with a long list of things you love/admire/respect about your spouse. Share the list with each other. Then come up with creative ways to keep communicating those things to your spouse and add new things to the list often.

> *"Encourage one another and build each other up,*
> *just as in fact you are doing"* (2 Thess. 5:11).

*Practice dying to yourself. Jesus commanded us to love God, then love others. If we take this command seriously in our marriage, then we need to be more concerned with loving our spouse than we are with having our own needs or desires met. Practice doing something selfless today that will benefit or bring joy to your spouse, without looking for something in return.

> *" Whoever wants to be my disciple must deny themselves*
> *and take up their cross and follow me"* (Matt. 16:24).

Men, take these words to heart:

<u>You are needed</u>. You are strong and you have what it takes to fight for and see victory in your family. God chose you to be the warrior for your family. You may feel like Gideon, whom God used to lead his army in a mighty victory. You can read his story in Judges 6. What you need to know is that Gideon did not act like a warrior. He was hiding in a wine press because he feared his

enemies. When God sent an angel to talk with him and call him to greatness, the angel addressed him with, *"The Lord is with you, mighty warrior"* (Judges 6:12). Gideon was acting cowardly, but the Lord did not see him as a coward. He saw him as a warrior. God used a man who was hiding from the enemy to lead the army in victory against that same enemy. There is an enemy who is trying to destroy you and your family. You are God's Gideon in your family. God has chosen YOU, and only you, to lead your family to victory over the enemy of your souls. Your victory is assured. You only need to stand up and fight!

Fighting for your marriage looks like recognizing where stereotypes have played a part. It looks like being intentional about sharing your feelings: The good, bad, and ugly. It looks like leaning in toward each other when things get tough as opposed to pulling away. It looks like doing everything in your power to come out on the other side of this chapter of your story stronger and more united as a couple. One step at a time.

Notes:

[1] Proverbs 5:19

[2] Proverbs 20:5

[3] David Boehi, Brent Nelson, Jeff Schulte, Lloyd Shadrach. Dennis Rainey, General editor, *Preparing for Marriage: the complete guide to help you discover God's plan for a lifetime of Love,* (Ventura, CA: Gospel Light, 1997), 220.

Chapter 12

Answering Questions like Adoption

"Always be prepared to give an answer to everyone who asks you to give the reason for the hope that you have."[1]

"He (Jesus) came to that which was his own, but his own did not receive him. Yet, to all who receive him, to those who believe in his name, he gave the right to become children of God – children born not of natural descent, nor of human decision or a husband's will, but born of God."[2]

When people ask...

Inevitably, people will ask. People ask how you are doing or they ask about your situation for different reasons. Maybe they are just curious. Maybe they genuinely care for you and want to offer a listening ear or shoulder to cry on. Others may not directly ask, but they will beat around the bush or they will ask something that scratches the surface of your emotions, and you will have an opportunity to respond. Will you be ready to respond well?

You have probably been the victim of someone who verbally vomited all over you. Some people have so much emotion stirring inside and they do not know how to process it in a healthy way. Inevitably, when turmoil brews, it reaches a boiling point and whomever is near will take the fall-out. God cautions us all over the Proverbs to use our words wisely.

"The tongue has the power of life and death" (Proverbs 18:21).

"A man of knowledge uses words with restraint, and a man of understanding is even-tempered. Even a fool is thought wise if he keeps silent, and discerning if he holds his tongue" (Proverbs 17:27-28).

I know that you do not want to be the one who hurts others because of your own pain or turmoil. This is why it is so important to be prepared for when people ask about this sensitive subject. Peter gives us good advice in 1 Peter 3:15:

"Always be prepared to give an answer to everyone who asks you to give the reason for the hope that you have."

The title of this book is <u>Hope Deferred</u>. It is my HOPE that as you have walked through the pages of this book with me, you have learned how to have a hope that cannot be deferred. When our hope (our expectation or desire for something to happen) is placed in God and Him alone, we will never have our hope deferred. He will always fulfill us. We will never be disappointed when our hope is in Him. Hopefully, the truth in this book will help you be prepared to give a reason for the hope that you have. Hopefully, you are filled with a deeper hope than you have ever known possible. Did I say *hopefully* enough times?

So as we close out our time together, I wanted to look at some of the common scenarios that those of us who are desiring to conceive find ourselves. I hope that as you look at these situations, you will *"be prepared to give an answer to everyone who asks."*

The proverbial: How are you doing?

Most of the time, when people ask this question, they really are not interested in your answer and they probably do not plan to listen to it. It is really more of an extended greeting than an actual question. They assume you will say "good," and the two of you will move on in the conversation. I have a real disinterest for fakeness and, as a result, when I greet someone with that question, I genuinely want to hear the answer. When someone asks me that question, I try to make an effort to honestly share how I am doing. I have a few people in my life with whom I have learned not to put much energy into my answer. I still answer honestly, but I do not exert even the tiniest amount of mental energy because I know that it will be wasted on them. They just do not really care or take the time to listen - or maybe they are not used to receiving an honest answer. It is helpful to gauge who the people are in your life who genuinely care, who genuinely want to share in your suffering and/or rejoicing. It is in your best interest to make a conscious effort with these people to be real about how you are doing. Let them in. Do not try to walk this journey alone. Do not let the enemy succeed in isolating you.

So how are you doing? <u>Possible positive but honest answers</u>: Okay. Pretty good. Hanging in there. Good. Decent. Thankful. Struggling, but I know I will win the fight.

The unsuspecting: "Oh, I didn't know you guys were having a hard time getting pregnant."

The awkward silence hangs in the room as the one who just declared the statement realizes that they may have crossed an invisible line. They have no idea how sensitive you are regarding this subject. How will you respond? You want to practice giving people the benefit of the doubt whenever you find yourself with the door to your emotional journey flung wide open. It is in your best interest, and the most loving option, to assume that the person who just opened the door to your emotions did not mean to make things uncomfortable for you. They may even be asking for a deeper relationship with you. They may want the opportunity to share their own journey or struggles. Be careful not to throw your guard up too permanently when something triggers your emotions. Otherwise, you may miss out on growing deeper with someone. Let the Holy Spirit guide you as to how much of your journey you should share. You do not want to miss out on ministering to their heart or having them minister to yours. Colossians 4:5 says:

"Make the most of every opportunity"

The innocent grandparents: When are we going to have some grand babies from you two?

How much you let your folks in on your journey depends on what kind of a relationship you have with them. Unfortunately, some parents have not been able to be the loving, supportive parents that we all need. If that is your case, it may be wise to allow the vulnerable and raw emotions that surface on this journey to be saved for you and your husband to navigate together. On the other hand, as you invite people into this journey with you, you may be amazed at some healing that God brings to your relationships. You are the best one to discern which scenario is best for you. The Holy Spirit will guide you, too. Your parents may not be the type to ask. In which case, prayerfully consider whether or not bringing up your infertility journey with them might provide an opportunity to grow in relationship with them. If your parents are followers of Jesus, you may want to ask them to pray for you. If they are not believers, it may provide an opportunity for you to show them how you have wrestled with God and are choosing to cling to him through this storm.

The high school reunion scenario:

You run into someone you haven't seen in a long time. Inevitably, a few of the first questions that come up: Are you married? Do you have any kids? Are you working?

Their questions are innocent and most likely born out of curiosity. But as we know, high school was the prime time of comparison. We stacked ourselves up against everyone we knew to determine our worth. Some of those old habits linger and we find that our self worth takes a blow when we encounter someone from the past who we perceive as being better off than us in one area or another. You can protect yourself in this situation by daily practicing thankfulness. The more thankful you are for your lot in life, the less likely you are to be enticed by what others have.

Remember that God has different purposes for each one of us. Success and failure as determined by the world do not usually line up with God's definition of those two words.

The "it's not really about you" scenario:

You know which scenario I'm talking about. You decide to let someone in and share a little bit of your journey and suddenly you realize that you are no longer talking about you. Your conversation partner is going on and on about when she experienced something similar and how she got through it. Some people have not had enough practice at listening well. That does not have to be you. If someone launches into their own story instead of just letting you share your heart, there is an opportunity for you to listen to their heart. Maybe they are sharing with you because they have something that is not yet resolved. Or maybe they are just uncomfortable with the tiny piece of realness you shared with them. Do not give up. Have patience. You may be the tool that God uses to help that person become more comfortable with the raw, real parts of life. Yes, it is another opportunity to die to yourself, too.

The person with all the advice:

"The way of fools seems right to them, but the wise listen to advice."
(Proverbs 12:15)

It is wise to take advice, but you want to make sure that the advice you receive is from a credible and reliable source. I am sure you have a few friends who seem to go to everyone they know for advice and, in the end, they end up so confused and paralyzed that they cannot move forward. Check out the fruit in the life of the person who is giving you advice. What situations has that person been through, and what were the outcomes? Does this person live life with freedom and joy, or is this person stressed out and worried much of the time? Has this person been trustworthy in advice they have given in the past? If you see that the person offering you advice is trustworthy, then, by all means, takes their words to heart, but do not stop there. God has given us the most important Counselor and advice-giver to live inside of us, the Holy Spirit.[3] Try to listen to that inner voice of discernment so that you can filter what the person has said to you against what God's Word says. The Holy Spirit speaks in the language of the Word of God. They are One: The Word (Jesus), the Father, and the Spirit.

Have you considered adoption?

Remember my dear friend, Chris, who miscarried many times and lost her baby at 34 weeks when she was 45 years old? When she was on her 5th round of in-vitro, she admitted to me that she would get discouraged when people asked her if she and her husband had considered adoption. She knew that people meant well when they asked, and she had no reservations about adopting, but to her, it felt as if people had given up hope that she would be able to carry a child in her womb. She was not ready to give up trying to carry a child and, thus, she did not want others to give up either. When my friend was 47, she delivered a beautiful, healthy baby girl. Despite urging from well-meaning friends, Chris did not give up. She believed that her story included a healthy child from her womb. Praise God for his miracle in her life!

Chris's baby girl was the last frozen embryo. Chris and Paul had reached the end of the line for them. They had decided that if this pregnancy did not take, they were ready to pursue adopting. Their hearts were genuinely surrendered for any outcome. They trusted the One who was writing their story. Their story is a gripping one. It is important to note that Chris and Paul were on the same page about how far and how long they would pursue trying to have a child from their womb before looking into adoption. For Chris and Paul, adoption was something they would consider if they hit the end of the road in their attempts to conceive a child. They knew the end of the road for them was when they ran out of embryos on the last round of in-vitro. For some people, the end of the road comes much sooner or, for others, the call to adopt is placed heavily on their hearts before they realize infertility is even an issue.

Most of the time, if someone asks if you have considered adoption, it is because they are curious. They probably want to know where your convictions lie. They want to know how you see your story panning out. They want to know how long you will hold out for trying to have a child from your womb. Or they may just want to try to fix your situation for you...which I find a little funny. You never knew adoption might be an option? ...and even if adoption is something you have considered, it doesn't change the fact that you also have a desire to carry a baby in your womb. Adoption doesn't fix that. Adoption is a beautiful thing. It is also a very complicated thing.

If you think you may have hit the end of the road in your pursuit of carrying a child in your womb, then let's talk a little more about adoption. In order to have a well-prepared response to inquiries regarding adoption, it is helpful to first have a clear understanding of the beauty of adoption and God's desire for your family. Any reservation one might have toward adoption is due to the fact that it was God's original design that every woman be able to carry a child in her womb. It was also God's original design that a woman would raise the child she carried in her womb. It was not God's intention that any woman experience barrenness, nor was it His design that any baby or child ever experience life without a loving mom and dad. His heart breaks for all of the little lives who do not have anyone to love them, nurture them, and care for them. The world we live in shows an abundant need for children to be adopted into loving, nurturing, and life-sustaining homes. God puts the desire for adoption on the hearts of His followers to help meet these needs. Has He given you that desire? James 1:27 says,

> *"Religion that God our Father accepts as pure and faultless is this:*
> *to look after orphans and widows in their distress*
> *and to keep oneself from being polluted by the world."*

God's idea of religion inherently implies caring for those who do not have anyone else to care for them. It means wearing love as a garment and refusing to fall prey to the ways of the world that pollute us and prevent us from meeting the needs of others.

Adoption was God's idea first. Adoption is a key part of our story as followers of Jesus.

In ancient days, the nation of Israel was known for being the children of God. They were God's chosen people. However, time and time again, they rebelled against God. They gave in to the pressure from surrounding nations, and they did things that hurt God's heart, including choosing allegiance to the lesser gods of these other nations. God has shown us their story throughout the Bible in order to show us the beauty of his forgiving nature and to show us that *who* we are is more important than *where we have come from*.

Romans 9:6-9 says,

> *"For not all who are descended from Israel are Israel. Not because they are his descendants are they all Abraham's children. On the contrary, 'It is through*

229

Isaac that your offspring will be reckoned.' In other words, it is not the natural children who are God's children, but it is the children of the promise who are regarded as Abraham's offspring. For this was how the promise was stated: 'At the appointed time I will return, and Sarah will have a son."

This verse is a little confusing for me, but it helps us see that God's true children are His spiritual children – not just children who share Israel's bloodlines. We have talked about Sarah. She was VERY old, yet God gave her and her husband a son, Isaac. God chose Abraham's offspring to be His chosen people, but this passage shows us that Isaac's "offspring" did not refer merely to the children that would share the same bloodline. For God, it is not about common DNA, it is about the heart. The people that you share a bloodline with do not dictate your place in this world or the one to come. When Jesus entered the picture, Jesus became the blood that united all people, not just those of a certain nationality. God says, *"There is neither Jew nor Greek, slave nor free, male nor female, for you are all one in Christ Jesus"* (Galatians 3:28).

John 1:11-13 (parenthesis added) puts it this way: *"He (Jesus) came to that which was his own (the chosen bloodline), but his own did not receive him. Yet, to all who receive him, to those who believe in his name, he gave the right to become children of God – children born not of natural descent, nor of human decision or a husband's will, but born of God."*

As Jesus' followers, we are all included in one massive family. We have been adopted into the family of God. If you have been spiritually "reborn," then you are included in the family of God. All people are God's children, but not all have accepted God's son, Jesus. It is through Jesus that we are adopted and have the opportunity to take part in benefits of having been included in the family of God. Spiritually speaking, God has offered the opportunity to be adopted into the family of God to everyone. It is up to us to choose whether or not we will accept that offer. If we refuse His offer, we miss out on the benefits of being a part of His family - with a loving Father as the head.

In a very real physical sense, there are millions of orphans who would love to be adopted into a family, but they just need the invitation. This is one of the reasons adoption is a beautiful thing.

So if your journey of desiring a child includes receiving a child into your home that was born from the womb of another as opposed to your womb, then I celebrate with you! The child you hold now, or will hold later, has been hand-picked by God to be a part of your earthly family.

If you are not sure whether or not your journey includes adoption, that is okay. It is a decision that needs to be made carefully and prayerfully. I hope you can firmly agree with me, as God has shown us in His much bigger story, that there is no difference in your heart between a child you receive from another womb and a child you receive from your own womb. They both come from God's womb. All are one in Christ Jesus. Neither is more important or valuable than the other – they are just different. I want to be careful not to minimize the struggles that can come with adoption, but as it pertains to God's gift to you, both are gifts.

The list of possible encounters or questions in this chapter is not complete or extensive. I am sure you have already had several memorable (and not necessarily in a good way) conversations and encounters that are a direct result of the path of infertility. You do not have to answer everyone perfectly. Just be as real and honest as you feel is wise in the moment and know that there is a loving God who understands the depths of your heart. Remember that you are not alone.

The Counselor – the Holy Spirit – your invaluable tool and friend.

"I will ask the Father, and he will give you another Counselor to be with you forever...the counselor, the Holy Spirit, whom the Father will send in my name, will teach you all things and will remind you of everything I have said to you" (John14:16 & 26).

A good counselor does not usually say a whole lot, but listens well. Their job is to guide you to process your situation so that you can end up in an emotionally good place when all is said and done. A good counselor asks good questions and watches the external processing unfold. They guide you from the outside as they watch which paths you go down mentally. A good counselor offers truth if you need a replacement for a lie and redirects your thinking when needed. A good counselor empowers you to become all that you need to become so you are no longer dependent on them to show you what is right and help you make decisions. Their goal is to move you to a place where you are making good choices on your own.

When it comes to the Holy Spirit being our Counselor, His goals are the same: To empower you and teach you how to walk in God's ways. His goal, however, is not to get us to a place where we do not need Him. We will always need His guidance, but the more that He trains us from the inside out, the more we begin to walk in freedom and truth as a natural way of life. As He counsels us, we take on more of the likeness of God and we naturally do the things that please Him and bring life to us and those around us. 2 Corinthians 3:18 tells us that we are becoming more and more like God through his Spirit. That is the goal: That we be like God. We were made to be like Him. God is currently in the process of restoring His creation back to the way it was created to function. The added bonus is that He is doing this good work in us from the inside out. His Spirit lives IN those of us who follow Jesus. We do not have a counselor who is just an onlooker in our journey. We have a Counselor that is literally walking with us and knows our every thought.

With the Spirit of God on the inside, He is the best qualified to guide you. He will counsel you about how to respond to those who will ask. He will counsel you and your spouse about what decisions need to be made each step of the way. Your job is to listen to the counsel. Do not deafen your ears to his voice. He speaks the language of love: Love for God, love for others, and also love for self. No matter where you are headed, you do not go alone.

So as we close this book, I want to hold out one more promise from God's word. I'm thankful that the Holy Spirit is the Counselor, and I know that He will counsel you about this verse.

> *"He settles the barren woman in her home*
> *as a happy mother of children"* (Psalm 113:9).

I do not know if you will find yourself settled in your home with children from your womb or if you will be happily settled with children God hand-picked for you from another womb. What I do know is that He will fulfill your desire for a child, and He will counsel you about how He will fulfill that desire if you will listen.

Conclusion:

This path is not for the faint at heart. It takes courage and perseverance to move forward on the terrain of desiring a child. You must take your thoughts captive. You must cling to the truth. You must do everything you can to stay alive in your heart.

You are not alone. It may sometimes feel lonely, but you are not alone. You have God's Spirit living in you if you follow Jesus. Also, there are many others who have experienced the highs and lows of desiring a child. The way to successfully and joyfully navigate this path marked out for you is to refrain from placing your hope in other people or in their stories. Similarly, the key to victory is not found with your hope firmly rooted in getting pregnant. The key to victory is to learn to orient your heart toward placing your hope in God.

His heart is for you. His heart is pro-children. I cannot make any guarantees that you will get pregnant, but I believe God wants you to have a child. It is His heart. Give me your argument for the contrary and I will argue that much stronger that God's heart, the way He engineered us, to the core of who we are, is to be moms (if that is your desire). I would argue that His heart is for you to be a mom. God loves children. He values them.

God works miracles. Whether or not we see the manifestation of the miracle now or later is unknown. I have seen him work miracles. I have seen the barren become fertile. I have seen those who have been told, "You will never have a child," holding a child from their own womb. I have held two children in my arms that I was not supposed to be able to conceive. I have seen those who think they are too old become a modern day Sarah. I am still praying for a friend who entered menopause in her twenties. I am praying for a friend who married later in life and desperately wants to be a mom. I am praying for a few friends who are not married yet, but desperately desire this. I am praying for you. I am praying that those on this path do not let fear overcome them.

I have also seen the miraculous in those who have embraced a different story for their lives than the ones they originally sketched. Through opening their hearts to foster care and adoption, I have truly seen beauty rise from the ashes. Foster care and adoption bring their own set of struggles along with so many beautiful aspects as multiple stories unite.

I sincerely hope that you found some truth in the pages of this book that will help you walk victoriously, freely, and with hope on this journey. I hope that God has encouraged you and strengthened you. I challenge you to *remember*. Do whatever it takes to fight for what is good and right and true and remember what God has taught you. Remember the truths that have caused your sight to be clearer. Remember to delight in God, being thankful. And remember to keep your hope in Him.

> *"Hope deferred makes the heart grow sick,*
> *but a longing fulfilled is a tree of life"* (Proverbs 13:12).

God has planted a seed in you...will you water it and tend to it, that it may grow into a flourishing tree?

> *"They will be like a tree planted by the water that sends out its*
> *roots by the stream. It does not fear when heat comes;*
> *its leaves are always green. It has no worries in a year of drought*
> *and never fails to bear fruit"* (Jeremiah 17:8).

Notes:

[1] 1 Peter 3:15

[2] John 1:11-13 (parenthesis added)

[3] John 14:16, 26

Afterword

Thank you for allowing me to share pieces of my story with you. I wrote this book as the guidebook that I wish I had had when I was walking the path of infertility. When I was in the thick of it, I wanted to know that someone else understood, and I wanted someone who would encourage me to grow closer to God through it, instead of pull away.

It has not always been pretty. At times, I have failed miserably at clinging to the truth God has taught me. At other times, I fought hard and found the peace that surpasses understanding. What you have in this book is the collection of lessons God has taught me through infertility. I tried to communicate these pearls of wisdom as best as I could. Hopefully you took note of when the Holy Spirit was speaking to you. Allow me to quote G.I. Joe again: *Knowing is half the battle.* Now is the time to hold on to the truth God has spoken to you and put it into practice. Now is the time for action.

I imagine you picked up this book because you still have hope for pregnancy. I want you to know that I hope for that with you. I really believe that in a perfect world, the original world God created, you would not have any problem getting pregnant. I also recognize that this world is currently still broken.

God wants us to participate with Him in helping this broken world become whole again. Wherever we see brokenness and dysfunction, God wants to use us to bring healing and restoration. Sometimes we have to fight through great darkness before we see the light break through. We each have different battles to fight and opportunities before us to usher in more of God's goodness. Infertility is one of those battles we have in common.

I am convinced that God wants to do something good in you and through you. Asking God for a miracle, for Him to help you conceive, is a good thing. You can continue to hope for a child from your womb and at the same time be completely surrendered to God and the plans He has for you. If you are surrendered, then God will either encourage you to keep hoping for a miracle from your womb or He will change your heart and your desires. He can only change your heart if you let Him. Like a potter with clay, you have to be moldable. If you are moldable, something great is going to come out of it.

At the end of the day, our stories WILL look different. Our stories will look different from each other. There is a good chance our stories will look different than the story we have mapped out in our minds. What matters most is whether or not we trust the Author to write a good narrative, while we are in the middle of the story.

Thank you for allowing me to walk alongside you on your journey and for allowing me to share what God has taught me. I am confident that God has imparted some pearls of wisdom to you in your journey as well. I would love to hear about them, and I would love to hear how God has used this book to encourage you. If you feel up for sharing, you can email me at: hopedeferred-book@gmail.com.

239

About the author

Jillian began her personal battle with infertility in 2007, and has since walked alongside many other couples whose lives have been affected by infertility. Although infertility was a huge part of her journey for many years, it is only part of the story.

Jillian graduated from Western Michigan University with a degree in Secondary Education and Spanish, with a minor in Family Life Education. Immediately upon finishing her student teaching and graduation, she joined the staff of the campus ministry that introduced her to Jesus as a college student. She worked for 5 years as a campus minister before choosing to stay home with her firstborn, who was 2 at the time.

Jillian lives in Southwest Michigan with her husband, Todd, and their 4 children. She is currently a work (stay) at home mom. She enjoys being a mom - although she admittedly is not hard-wired to be a stay at home mom. She is grateful for the opportunity to raise and shape these special children. Her oldest is in 8th grade, followed by a fourth grader, then a 5 year old, and lastly a 3 year old.

In the years since choosing to stay home, Jillian has led youth group and several bible studies as well as volunteering in her community. She also rides horses, gives horse back riding lessons, dabbles in photography, and has been known to set up shop at a few local craft shows, in addition to writing.

Jillian has always felt compelled to encourage others and mentor those who are walking similar paths that she has walked in hopes of making their journey a little easier. This book and her blog are a product of that compulsion.

To learn more about Jillian and to view more of her writing, check our her web site: www.unwaveringhope.com. You can also find her on Instagram or Twitter @Jillian_Heerlyn or on her Facebook Author Page: Jillian Heerlyn.